Moy McCrory

was born in Liverpool and ~~~~~~~~~~~~~~~
Belfast. She now lives in Salis~~~~~~~~~~~~~~~
two volumes of short stories. *~~~~ Water's Eage* and
Bleeding Sinners. The latter was described by the *Irish
Times* as 'generous and compassionate, and to coin a
phrase, bloody marvellous'. This is her first novel.

v

By the same author

The Water's Edge (Stories)
Bleeding Sinners (Stories)

Moy McCrory

The Fading Shrine

Flamingo

An Imprint of HarperCollinsPublishers

Flamingo
An Imprint of HarperCollins*Publishers*
77–85 Fulham Palace Road,
Hammersmith, London W6 8JB

Published by Flamingo 1991
9 8 7 6 5 4 3 2 1

First published in Great Britain by
Jonathan Cape Ltd 1990

The quotation on page v is taken from Medieval Latin Lyrics,
(1933) fourth edition, by Helen Jane Waddell, published by
Constable and Co. Ltd. The lines on page 171 are taken from
'Breakin' Down the Walls of Heartache', Linzer/Randell © 1968
Screen Gems-EMI Music Inc, USA. Reproduced by permission
of Screen Gems-EMI Music Ltd, London WC2H 0EA

Printed in Great Britain by
HarperCollins Manufacturing, Glasgow

In the year of the incarnation of Our Lord 900 there appeared a marvellous sign in Heaven, for the stars were seen to flow from the very height of Heaven to the lowest horizon well nigh as though they crashed one upon the other. And upon this marvel followed woeful calamities such as a most notable untowardness of the seasons and frequent tempests, rivers also overflowing their banks as in dread likeness of the deluge and what was yet more pestilent than these, ominous upheavals of men boasting themselves against God.

Radbod (a tenth-century cleric)

CONTENTS

PART ONE

THE OUTLINES
APPEAR

I

THE CONVENT OF
FORTITUDE

It being the mass day of the martyrs Cyprianus and Cornelius, the sea swelled up and rose upon the shore and buried houses whole and very many oxen and sheep were lost. In some parts, men walking were thrown to the ground and church roofs split. The bells behind the market-place rang four times as the earth tilted.

The morrow after Crouchmas Day, fiery monsters were seen in Heaven and fire crackled and spewed from rocks. Then followed a most marvellous storm of light blinding to the eyes and roaring in the head. With a terrible crashing, trees were rent in two, torn as a blade of grass is between finger and thumb.

People were driven to strangeness; like demented creatures they ran outdoors, some naked. They screamed and clawed like beasts towards the church, where they thought to appease the Lord's anger. Throughout that night green and bluish lights were seen by many as Heaven opened, but there were those who said it was the awfulness of Hell. After, such hail fell as has never been seen on earth until this day. Stones as big as loaves dropped out of the sky. Labourers in the field were caught, three killed and not a soul might collect their corpses until a week was past. All feared to be abroad.

Then rain, a solid curtain of glass as at the parting of the sea. Birds could not lift up their wings against it. Eaves and roofs could not hold, beams snapped. In the village a weight of water brought down mud walls. The one bright window in our chapel shattered.

Many thought that Doomsday had come. By praying we thought to be ready for the final judgment. Men waited for the soil to wash away from graves when they might see the corpses walk again. The gate to our plot was open so the dead might pass freely as those departed sisters were given the command, 'Rise up!' like Lazarus. But this did not happen.

In a time given to unnatural sightings, astronomers saw new stars and there were many witnesses to the marvels. It is written how men were born with four legs like rams, how fish swam in the sky and fire lit upon trees. The woodman returning with his bundles told how he heard the tongue of the Devil in the market-place, words spoken backwards so no Christian could understand and the name of Satan was on men's lips. Brother turned upon brother, parents upon their own children and good men denounced their wives. Throughout the world was much confusion and the Antichrist was said to have come.

Outside the Convent of Fortitude four common women pulled twice on the bell-rope and waited. Loud and echoing, they heard it resound in the yard as they stood silently in the downpour clutching their meagre garments about themselves.

All that week it had rained. Each morning the tiller looked towards the sky and saw heavy black clouds approaching from the east, swollen with water the satiated earth could not use. Like a drunkard when full blown in his cups and spread-eagled on the tavern's floor, the soil lay in abandon, river-bloated and sucking.

Autumn was the time for soil, for dredging, furrowing and trampling. All hands were needed, yet these women could not stay.

Two were widows, their husbands taken in the last raid by white strangers from the north, another was married, and the youngest of them knew no man, but had been foolish enough to fall asleep with the moon on her face and later felt its ripe night-seed take shape in her belly.

Before a day's labour started, before the first fire was re-kindled and the oven in the village lit, they had met in the market-place. Without speaking they knew each other's condition. They knew they must be cleansed. In silence they left the village together.

As they walked, their feet sunk into the heavy earth. They pulled each dull step relentlessly, and if one could not continue or fell face down, they were roughly pulled up, kicked into a plod behind the others.

At dusk they approached the forest where robbers lived, and worse, wood spirits who took your heart while you slept or made you captive by twisting their branches about your neck. They knew of the great tree whose roots went down to the heat of Hell and whose topmost branches brushed the feet of angels.

Between them they carried one small knife, sharp as murder. It glinted, dripping in the night dryness as the forest floor crackled where dense trees let no rain through. Exhausted and famished, they would not stop to rest, fearing to stretch out on the dry ground. They walked vigilantly through the night and their eyes tore gaps in the dark.

They saw shapes and shadows. Were these souls who twisted in torment, as branches acted out their tableau against sky? Clinging together they passed the outstretched, giant hands of those who beckoned them to judgment.

When finally the sky lightened, a mist swirled about their legs, the ground smoked with cold. They came to a place where the trees were less tightly packed and between roots the soil formed into frozen ridges of mud where rain had softened the ground.

In front of them the land opened on to the plain they had heard their shepherds speak of, and on the higher ground beyond, they saw something. As the morning lifted the outline of roofs appeared. Far off and still a day's distance was the double monastery of the martyrs.

It was a split site of brothers and sisters dedicated to a life of prayer. A church belonged in common to the orders, the only building they were ever in together, otherwise they existed either side of a great wall. They entered the church of Saint Polycarp through their own side doors to sit on opposite sides of a central wooden screen. The order never saw its mirror reflection, but could hear the strangeness of the masculine voices at service, while the men in turn listened to the lightness of the women joining in the response.

The Convent of Fortitude's buildings lay to the left of the dividing wall and although the monastery on the right was equal sized, the nuns remained in its shadow, for it wielded more power than any order of women could. The nuns continued in autonomy, trusting in the protection their site offered them and praying that the one and only door between them would continue to be unlocked only in the interests of commerce.

From a distance the double monastery with its great central wall looked as if some angry giant had driven a hatchet between the land causing two islands to result, which could never be joined.

With this in their sights the travellers rested, falling on the ground in pain. They had no protection from the cold and as they lay still their legs stung and their skin was blue and mottled. Even with such exhaustion it was easier to keep moving so they did not rest for long and by evening had reached the outer wall of the foundation.

It was a wall which cut the world in half and represented the end of all life. They knew the rumours. In the village they said that to pass it, first one must die; but they walked towards it.

Set into one side of the wall was a heavy wooden turn-gate. They touched it carefully. It was motionless. A huge semi-circle of solid black panels, that was curved like a barrel and sightless. This was the unofficial entrance to the women's side, the hidden way into the Convent of Fortitude.

The common women waited. They heard the bell inside and each wondered what was behind the wall, if an echo might roll around as in the great open sky that covers all earth.

Hearsay had brought them so far. They did not know if their journey would prove hopeless. They would ask the nuns for charity until their time; they had nowhere else.

From inside there was a grating sound as bolts drew back. The heavy turn-gate began to move. It revolved awkwardly, stopping and restarting, it dragged as it was cranked through a complete circle. When it slowly swung round the women grabbed each other's hands in fright. The heavy wooden gate revolved, revealing a row of shelves, stacked one upon the other.

The turn-gate was hollow like a drum and rotated from a central shaft. Its depth formed a series of cupboards which the nuns used to receive supplies from outside. Any other traffic must pass through the one connecting door between the sites under the eye of the abbot. But a different type of cargo was being sent into the convent, one for which the nuns need not barter. The gate grated to a halt.

The women stared at it. Through this gate everyone must pass. But the entrance was difficult and narrow. It had not been built to take bodies; a man would never fit, it would be hard enough for them. They became all shapes; they tried squatting, they bent double, or flattened themselves, contorting to squeeze inside the narrow shelves which were so close together that anyone lying on their back would feel their nose brush the underside of the one above.

The youngest woman watched the other three crawl in, but still she waited. She had heard tell that it was only through death they could enter the women's side, and she did not want to die.

'Get in you great cow. Do you want to return in disgrace?'

But she remained motionless, her eyes large with horror.

'They are like those coffins stacked up in the woodyard. I've seen them when I collect sawdust.'

'Go back then!' the bald widow said and spat at her. 'Find your own way back and die there instead.' She pointed to the way they had come. 'Die there. You could have saved yourself a journey.'

But still she hesitated. She looked back over her shoulder and saw the dark band of forest far in the distance, imagined the hopeless way through it and what would await her on the other side. Quivering, she plunged into the shelf and placed her knuckles into her eye sockets so that she might not see the face of death when it appeared.

The other widow knocked with her fist on the wood as she might on a closed door.

'Please, we're tired. We've coursed a day and night without rest to get here. We're desperate; some say defiled, even those that done it say so. Let us pass from this life into yours. We come to be cleansed, help us. Don't turn us back.'

The gate juddered, sending spasms of terror through them. They gripped their knees and lay sideways staring out towards home. Their eyes followed the darkening landscape as they hugged their worn rags about them and shivered. They lay curled as snail shells, cramped as corpses, and felt the gate being cranked strenuously. As it turned slowly through the great stone walls the women were plunged into darkness. They anticipated it, saw it creep up. The wall covered the opening as the gate moved through a full circle.

The youngest panicked and caught the wall with her fists so that her face would not be covered, but she was not strong enough to stop it. Her knuckles tore against the stones and she was taken into the wall shrieking.

Inside was the sightlessness of long nights, more desperate than the shadows of the forest for they did not know whether this would end. If there was no return, what would become of them here in this place? One of them began to moan. A semi-human growl it became in that tomb. As it escaped from her mouth the others froze. They had been tricked, now they were to be buried alive.

But gradually a pale strip began to appear at the bottom of each shelf. It widened as grey light seeped into the shelves and the gate span, bringing the four with it to enter the convent feet first like breechlings.

The women clambered out, wet clothes stuck to their skinny limbs and they trembled with cold and fear, too scared at first to look up and face the unknown. A huge courtyard opened through the gloom in front of them. The nun who operated the gate was nowhere to be seen. There were grey flagstones everywhere, all the yard was paved, just like the floor of the church at home. They had never seen such a floor in an open space. They peered around, wondered why there was no roof, saw how the stones made a clean walkway without sand and mud to squelch in, but smooth and shiny with the rain. They hobbled, frightened of slipping.

The only sound was the constant rain. It ran down gullies, directed away from the stone roofs of the buildings that sprawled in the distance across the yard. The church in their village had such gullies, and the roof, before it blew down, was slope-sided letting water spill off and race away. In the village it poured back on to earth tracks which were already awash with mud. In this place there were grooves cut out of the stone, the work of a master mason, which channelled the water away. The space the women were in seemed vast to them despite the heavy wall which stood between the monastery, separating the nuns from the monks.

In all the divided site, there was only one door to allow a priest through with viaticum, or bring in new entrants, or lead the cow through when she needed the service of a bull.

The monks knew there was no other entrance to the convent apart from an opening for sacks of meal and for trading. The turn-gate conveyed most things which the nuns needed; tools, for they had no smith, barrels when they needed them, even small sections of masonry.

To the monks the four did not exist as they stood looking

about. On the left of the convent there were low-lying buildings which looked like outhouses for barns and worksheds. Behind this was a small pasture, but the best land had been crossed by the women as they journeyed. The order owned the surrounding area and leased out fields so that by tithes and rents they had once been wealthy, but now the land yielded them little profit. Many people in their village worked for the convent; the candle-maker, the grain supplier and the vintner would all have been poorer without its custom.

When the women opened their eyes fully they saw that they were not in another kingdom. A mortal stood waiting. It must have been a mortal for no light came from its face, there was no music or sweet-smelling incense such as they had been promised. Its robes were not gleaming or of the finest costliest fabrics, not the rich velvets and deep purple shawls the priests spoke of, but were muddy and torn. The mortal one stood in the downpour, water running the length of its overlarge nose. Its skin was red and chapped. Its hands were ungainly; mannish. Hands that were used to hard work. The common women were its kindred. Not for their ears the choirs of angels as the lay sister watched them.

When she knew that they had all seen her, she put her finger to her lips for silence, then beckoned them to follow. She made no attempt to reassure them by nod, or smile, or gesture, but walked ahead and the women followed obediently as if they had been bred to take such discipline all their lives.

Of the four, only one was shod, in some poor leather sandals which were cut to pieces. All were bare-headed and their clothes were torn, their shifts threadbare. One already showed signs. Her ripe belly stuck out grandly as if to mock the poverty of the lifeless woman who bore it.

Shaking with cold, they were taken to a line of low buildings. An old nun waited at a door. Skeleton thin, she wore her wimple tightly knotted about her narrow face and without a word pointed inside, holding out a steady hand.

On entering they found themselves in a narrow room. It

was empty except for four bowls of water and four robes neatly folded on the floor. The women had been expected.

A door led from a side wall. This was closed and gave no hint of what lay behind. Torches blazed in each corner. As there were no slits in the walls for light the room was cold but without draughts. The old nun followed them and pointed to the water then left, closing the door to the outside softly behind her.

The women had never seen such clear water. They did not know if it was for them to drink; it seemed too good for washing. They laughed at the novelty, putting their hands in and seeing through it. They watched as soot and grime came off leaving their hands white and naked. They stepped out of their filthy rags and poured the sweet water over themselves, tasting it, hardly believing how refreshing it was. Rivulets made white streaks on their skin and they watched shyly, laughing at their companions as they appeared cleaner with every circular rub until their bodies glowed.

The air in the low room was fresh, no smells of dung, or pigs. They stood ashamed in their gleaming nakedness watching each other's bellies in silence in the cold room of luxury.

'These must be for us,' one of the widows said and lifted a black robe.

The married woman hissed for silence and all four looked around in case their error had been heard. They waited until the woman who first spoke shrugged and pulled the robe over herself. Her head came through the neck opening and she smoothed it down over her body, smiling. They followed her example, pulling the fabric over their heads, struggling with the fasteners at the waist, while each marvelled at the thickness of the material. Although the weave was coarse, the garments were warm and afforded them comfort such as they had never experienced.

They spoke not one word now, scared to disobey the first lay sister who had vanished.

When the old nun returned she brought with her two who wore the white robes of postulants. The women waited obediently. They could have been penitents or about to enter the convent apart from their signs of fecundity, for each naked had shown some increase to her belly, an increase that had not been brought about by nourishment.

The nun spoke brusquely, breaking the silence. They knew that talk was not free here and everything would be kept to a minimum of words.

'Come with me.'

She beckoned one of the women to come forward. As she led her from the room the postulants followed. The door closed behind them. The three left did not understand what they should do, but stood watching the wooden door as though in its gnarled and knotted wood they might discover an answer.

It was the married woman who went first. She was taken into a dark room, smaller than the last. There was a window. Through it the sky looked thunderous. Heavy clouds pressed the tops of trees. The woman peered about her curiously, noting the strange things she had no names for. In a recess was a huge chimney, the source of the wonderful warmth that she had felt as she entered. The fire burned with an orange heat. By its sparks and sputterings she discovered the room as the flames flared up periodically. She made out shapes in the quickly glowing moments.

Set into the fire were several pots, and metal rods glinted in a large steaming bowl. Hung over the fire was a rack with knives whose blades sparkled in the flames. Things also hung from the ceiling, bunches of dried herbs and pickling spices, but this was no kitchen. Then she saw the open barrels full of sawdust against the walls. She gasped and flexed her hands nervously then cupped them over her mouth to swallow her terror.

'Take this,' the smaller of the postulants said. But the

woman did not hear and continued to gaze round, frightened by unfamiliarity.

Strange objects lay discarded on the table, which was enormous, as big as any butcher's in the market, but, unlike those, this table was spread with bottles and long, upright bird feathers which stood in dark pots. There were pieces of sharp bone and brushes such as the potter used at home.

She had seen one book in her life. It was kept in church, and she had never seen inside it. But on this table there were at least four. She wondered that so many could have been written. This room was something between a kitchen and a church. It puzzled her.

'Drink this,' the little sister said handing her a cup.

The woman looked inside and hesitated.

'It's only an infusion to make you still.' She spoke softly, and the woman saw how her hands were white and smooth as she held the cup towards her.

The woman took it and sniffed. It smelt sweet, like nothing she knew of. She gulped the liquid down.

'I want more.' She did not know how to ask, but knew that it warmed her hungry belly, and she wanted that experience again.

'More,' she said, for she knew no other way.

Her cup was refilled and she drank noisily and greedily, feeling again the warm softness inside her swollen belly.

The old nun who had watched her in silence from the corner of the fire now approached. She indicated a straw pallet and the postulant helped the woman to lie on it.

'Lift up your robe,' the old nun said. It was an order, not a request.

The woman lay back on the straw, undignified and gross on her back with her distended guts upward.

'Are you hungry?' the nun asked.

The woman looked surprised.

'Always hungry,' she replied gruffly.

'After I have examined you, the Little Sister of Poverty

will take you down to the kitchen area. There you will be given food, not much, there is little enough we can spare, but enough to make you comfortable. Remember not to speak to the lay sister who waits on you.'

Food; the woman could not believe her fortune. Now she would do anything asked of her, and be grateful to do it. Even her dread of what would come paled as she contemplated the word. Food.

From a basket the old nun took a packet tied with a long string and placed it on the woman's belly. She crouched over the bulky form for a long while and listened with her ear against her gut. Then she drew herself up and held the packet by the length of string so that it hung down straight like a mason's plumb-line over the belly. The packet began to shake, then slowly it started to turn in circles, round and round it went smoothly and gathered up speed on each turn. The woman's eyes opened wide as it moved on its own in steady circles.

'It is the Devil!' she shrieked. But the old nun glanced at her angrily.

'I thought that was what you wanted. It is indeed the Devil's. The baby as yet is soulless. Come back to me tomorrow morning at first light; I will expect you then for the purging. Tonight you will be taken to a dry space in the outhouses where you may sleep.'

She pulled the robe down over the woman and walked away in the dark room without another word. The consultation was over.

2

AUTONOMY

It being the autumn of the year 904, the feast of Saint Odran.

The winter which ravaged the land, turned our pasture to lakes of mud wherein nought would grow, and left us a bad summer and scant harvest. We are weakened in body. All must glean for survival.

Our bell was left ringing, for we could give no succour to those outside. And in these lean times a further threat is made to our survival. Not only are our bodies put to the test, but now our hearts.

All about us small places give up to the large. The great order we freely follow would seek now to bring us to heel under the tutelage of the father house, to make us its lap dog, trained to carry out orders.

So the weaker is riddled by the stronger. But let us not forget that beneath the obedience of beasts lies the wild animal, waiting to snap through the tamed hide. How often does its coat bristle as man's hand pats it into shape?

On this account our abbess prepares to go from us. She will journey to our parent house, where all the heads assemble to see if this course might be averted by our actions.

Now I put aside this pen. I am instructed by my superior to act in her absence. May I be worthy of the task, and please God let nothing disturb the quiet of our days.

The strict rule of enclosure could only be relieved by such a letter as Aelreda the abbess held in her hand that morning. She received the well-sealed document grudgingly from the abbot who handed it through the communion grille in chapel. Both knew that the door between the sides would soon be unlocked. All heads were expected to leave their convents and travel to any of their order's houses if summoned.

Aelreda reread the letter. A great meeting was to be held at the Crown of Thorns, with all eight heads from the outlying communities. There had never been such a meeting.

Aelreda felt aggrieved. They faithfully followed the rule of Saint Benedict and she considered herself a strict head, or tried to be, and she was ever wary of new ideas which might threaten their existence. She was concerned about their herbalist's behaviour and wanted to challenge her. Furthermore, the reforming zeal, warned about in the document she held could mean disaster for them.

Her superior wrote that all convents on split sites might find themselves being governed by the abbots. Prohibited from clearing their internal difficulties themselves, and as a woman forbidden to enter the chapter house on the monks' side, Aelreda understood that this would remove any effective voice she might have in her convent's future.

And Mother Albergisten hinted that this might only be a first step. They could be deemed unworthy to follow the way of God without supervision. This to Aelreda meant more than simple interference in their ordered days; it meant the cessation of any autonomy they had retained through their founding charter. It was a move to undermine their very existence.

Later when the abbot suggested that a monk and one lay brother escort her some of the way to the parent house she might have laughed, if he could but guess the nature of the meeting. He offered as much help as he could and she accepted his offer graciously, wondering at how God worked.

The monk was journeying to one of their outreach sites to deliver a book. The nuns assembled a team; two lay sisters who would make preparations and would ride with Aelreda and two brothers to the next town. There a guide could be engaged and they would join in with a pilgrim party along a regular travel route for much of the journey for greater safety. All the party were granted a pardon to eat flesh-meat in the absence of all else and the lay sisters were excited at the prospect of a jaunt outside the walls.

Despite the necessity of the meeting, Aelreda felt no enthusiasm for the journey. She dreaded contamination by the outside world, and would have done anything to relinquish her responsibility if it saved her the torturous ride.

The world was foul and cruel and she no longer knew its habits. Entered as a child her entire experience of life was the convent and in it she was certain and knew its ways. She had no curiosity for the world, having no means of understanding what she saw. She was the least worldly of the house, for she had neither desire to witness it nor hear tell of it. She was frightened of the world outside; she did not know it well enough to hate it. To Aelreda it was foreign territory.

Despite all their precautions and the hiring of a guide of good reputation who was engaged to take the women right up to the convent gates, the nuns found themselves thrown together with various travellers, men and women of common ranks who thought nothing of doubling up in the hostelry.

At different stages in the journey people left and new ones joined. The sisters, unused to people, found the constant changing confusing. They were used to the same community every day and were disturbed by the seeming whirl of personalities as the faces spun around them like a juggler's coloured sacks.

Their guide, for all his recommendation, needed many gifts and tokens of appreciation before he would stir himself to make his charges comfortable. After the two brothers left on completion of their part of the journey, the sisters found it even harder to gain reasonable treatment, not being used to transacting deals like the monks. Despite their religious rank they frequently found themselves passed over in the allocation of warm sleeping spaces. It was the merchants and guildsmen among the travellers who gained the places nearest the fire and the best of the straw.

After the meditative way of the cloisters, life felt like a barrage of sound. Speech was louder, coarser and constant. People kept up unending discourse on all manner of things, even the quality of meat in one tavern compared to another. The abbess, trained in the sanctity of silence, found the talk wearisome. More than that, it was impossible to pray with all the different sounds crashing around and the distraction. She was constantly vigilant because here nothing was secure, not even her thoughts.

It was unwise to talk aloud, unwise to leave possessions down and so tempt trouble. The abbess was made to keep her small pack forever about her person, which was awkward and bothersome. At night the lay sisters had to keep watch in turns and rouse the others if they felt there was any danger or threat to their honour from a fellow traveller.

Aelreda wondered if she would ever be able to stop the habit of looking from the corners of her eyes. She decided that that was what gave the outside world dwellers their cruel, suspicious look; their eyes sideways-watching like cats, following every move.

She sat by the chimney corner and felt the heat spread through her chilled bones. It seemed to infuse her entire body. Her nostrils caught the scent of meat roasting and her belly ached with the need to fill it. Although physically tired she was still on guard and watched the remainder of the travelling party as they moved around the room at the hostelry. The lay sisters came to join her.

'We are to rest here,' Sister Martinus said looking around at the floor for the driest patch. 'After the supper is finished, the hosteller has agreed to send his men in with straw, although on such a cold night he cannot say whether we will be all the party as further travellers might be admitted as the night goes on.'

Already the burly hosteller and his wife were carrying out planks of wood and setting them across trestles in the middle of the great room. With much laughing and bawdy humour the task was completed with the assistance of the men in the party, who enjoyed teasing the hosteller's wife in a way which made her shake with laughter.

The travelling party was a rabble of different types. Now, with the monks gone, they were the only religious in the group and felt their difference all the more acutely. Other women in the company were either well chaperoned or travelled with their husbands, and in one group there was a noble-woman, who with great spirit joined in all the games at the end of the day. The common travellers did not mind the close proximity of each other's bodies at night, while to the abbess it was as great a risk of contamination to the spirit as the pestilence had been to the body.

The fire glowed orange and red, and the spit turned. The meat was already black, but inside, the abbess knew, it would be raw and hot with blood. Eating flesh-meat was a novelty to them, but now she would argue for as equal a share of it as any man in the party. Their strength had to be maintained.

People took up places at the table and the sisters saw that if they were not quick again their lot would be the furthest end, down-room in the draught, and the worst pickings from the titbit bowl when it reached them. How different was eating in the world. Instead of the silence and prayer reading at meals in the convent, here was activity based upon hunger, hunger against which these women had trained themselves by regular fasting. Now they were discovering appetite.

As they had journeyed southwards, food had become ever more plentiful. Leaving the starving regions behind, they discovered that in some towns stored wheat levels were still good, and wild meat was regularly obtained. Although breeding-stock meat had disappeared and there was scarcely a vegetable grown anywhere, gone was the privation of their own northerly region. Now the sisters ate as the rest did each day, a share of meat and bread, cutting with the knives that hung from their belts and had been unused for almost a year in the Convent of Fortitude as sisters grubbed like insects on berries and shoots.

With eagerness they approached the table, clambering over the benches and elbowing their way.

'This place is taken,' a huge man in calf leather breeches said, slapping his hand on the wood as the abbess, with one leg already over the bench straddled the seat.

'Unless you'd sit on my hand, say what?' He turned his palm outward and put out his tongue. On all sides of the table there was raucous laughter; men banged their thighs, slapped each other in jest and waited to see how she would react. She stood still, scared to lift her leg back across the bench.

'I'll fart on your hand instead then,' said another man coming up behind the nun to take her place. He lifted her easy as chaff over the wood while he spoke.

'Lest you're particular, we all blow the same.' He winked across the table, ignoring the nun who struggled to get into the space next to him.

The big man pulled his fist back sharply and laughed showing a mouth with broken spikes of teeth. His tongue was thick and pale lavender at the root as he stuck it out again, this time rolling his eyes.

'Why, good man, I was warming the seat for you,' and he clapped his back.

As the other sat, Aelreda found herself unable to take up the place, now that the man's massive backside had come down upon the bench. The travellers jostled each other and the nun could not squeeze in along that side of the table, but walked around to the head where the great man was putting on his brown, tanned apron.

The meat sat upon a pewter dish, steaming. The first opening would explode the rich fat which those closest to could dip their bread in. The man took his whet stone from his apron pocket, spat upon this and began to sharpen the large knife.

The daughter of the house carried eight round loaves on a wooden tray. Under her father's stern gaze she ignored the men's gibes and their pestering. She went round the table passing loaves over their shoulders. The abbess, standing behind, tore from one before it had reached the table and tucked the piece under her arm.

'What have you got up your skirts, pretty one?'

'I'd like to give her something to fill them out!'

The men nudged each other and laughed. They poked each other in the ribs until they were sore and slapped and pinched at the girl as she passed. She was swift, dodging their hands and bending away from them as she passed the loaves, experienced enough to know that she must not lean forward nor let anyone get behind her.

Suddenly there was a silence. The big man had put the stone down on the board and was testing the knife with a hair. All eyes turned to him as he positioned himself in front of the dish and the party's focus shifted from girl to head of table as the big man began to carve.

Slowly he raised the knife with his right hand, and with a sharp stick in his left he caught the meat and held it firmly. The knife seemed to wait, held aloft as a pennant knowing that each eye watched it. Then it came down and with regular sawing movements the big man moved it back and forth. Rhythmically the knife cut through the crisp, black surface. The first slice peeled away, pink and bloody inside. Steam rose from the split skin. Without stopping, his arm worked to slit ever nearer to the bone as the finer pieces came away and lay along the dish.

Straightening up he wiped the sweat from his brow with the back of his fat arm and indicated to those at the table's head to pass the first lot of meat down among them.

Aelreda watched over their shoulders as the first dish went along the wooden boards. She salivated, even for a scrap of gristle. She did not expect a good piece. Suddenly a hand reached back and thrust her a well burned morsel. Both lay sisters had managed to squeeze in at the table's head. They were so tightly wedged they could not move to let their superior sit without risking the loss of their places, but as soon as they held the plate they selected the best piece they could and passed it back. She took the meat quickly, and with her bread returned to the chimney seat where she was without doubt the warmest person in the room and could observe without being the object of ridicule.

She enjoyed the warmth while she could. She knew she would not find herself sleeping there, but would be removed to some cold corner of the room. Unused to the ways of bribery and unable to offer indulgences, the sisters fared badly. It was not that they were treated any worse than other members of the party, but neither were they shown any special consideration.

3

DECISION

IT WAS MIDWINTER WHEN the party from the Convent of Fortitude was received into Crown of Thorns. They were the last to arrive, having travelled the greatest distance. The abbess' relief on finding herself inside a walled world was shocking as tension fled from her. She sank back into the only society she understood which, although in another place, was a mirror reflection of her own.

Where the rule was lived, language had no boundary. In this convent were sisters from far places, dark skinned and speaking a nasal Latin, but they were united in the spirit despite all their apparent differences. It was a world that she understood, with clear rules, where decisions about day-to-day existence were not difficult as they were in the greater unstructured outer world, the wild terrifying place into which they had been cast after the fall.

She was summoned to the discussion immediately she had rested and washed, for the nuns had started that week in her absence.

As she walked along the stone passage towards the gathering she could hear voices raised; a babble of sounds and shouting. For a moment she felt as if she were back on the outside and her heart shrank until she reminded herself that here were her sisters in God, voices raised only in dignified protest.

In the chapter house Mother Albergisten banged a wooden mallet furiously on the table. Her old hands shook and she leaned on the chair-back for support. She peered short sightedly at the bottom of the table where the faces were nothing more than a blur.

'Silence! Silence!' she shouted hoarsely.

Immediately the noisy debate ceased. Her position as Supreme Head of the Faithful Sufferentia meant that her low voice was still the one which was most often heard.

She pulled herself up straight in an effort to address those furthest from her, as well as those close enough to hear with ease.

'If we do not implement some of the new reforming measures which are sweeping all foundations, if we do not agree to become accountable, at least to those abbots who are known to be lenient throughout our split sites, then our smallest convents will be lost first. They will be moved aside as those on double monastery grounds will find it impossible to govern themselves, and I fear that if we choose to ignore these signs we shall lose recognition from the great orders. Without this we will cease to exist in any form. Surely this is the greatest threat.'

She looked around for signs of agreement. Some nuns nodded their heads, while others remained impassive.

'What say you Mother Beatitude?' She turned to the elderly nun, who had maintained the superior's line of argument throughout the impassioned debate of the last days.

'I say that it is better to surrender some of our autonomy now, in the hope of the order surviving, rather than stand fast and possibly lose everything. To ignore this warning will bring about the total destruction of everything we have struggled to establish. Surely we cannot risk this?'

Of the assembled group, five of the eldest nodded their heads in agreement.

Here were all the delegations that had travelled from the outreach houses, not only the abbesses, but the learned nuns; the best scribe from the House of Perpetual Light, the choir mistress from Crown of Thorns, and their leading theologians. They numbered fifteen in all. It was an awesome gathering the young abbess was to join.

Mother Albergisten had gathered round her certain nuns who were agreeable to the recommendations she felt they must make. At the bottom of the table the opposition formed, furthest from her vision. It was from this group that a voice broke out unchecked.

'And what would we be then. Would we go under another banner? Perhaps we should change our habit to some lighter stuff already? Who knows how the monasteries will allow us to continue.'

At the far end of the table there was much movement with words of agreement and laughter. Encouraged the voice went on.

'We'll be known as white sisters then.'

Mother Superior brought her mallet down hard upon the wood.

'Permission to speak has not been granted,' she croaked at the nun who had replied to Beatitude's rhetorical question.

'And it is not granted.'

There was a creaking of chairs as several of the nuns straightened up uneasily. There were mutterings of agreement with the censored speaker. The nun who spoke clutched the wooden figure on the crucifix she wore and rubbed her fingers backwards and forwards over its surface. She looked down at her lap and her face looked brighter than usual. Next to her another shrugged her shoulders in resignation. Hands waved in the air for permission to speak, but these were ignored as Mother Superior continued.

'No one is suggesting that we abandon our Rule,' she repeated for the hundredth time that day. 'Only that it is lived in accordance with the greater institutions. And that as a mark of this we accept the need for greater accountability to the monasteries. We can no longer be totally independent. We must make a show at least of taking on some of these reforms.'

She sat down heavily, exhausted by the effort of managing the discussion. She needed someone to sum up for her, to put into neat words all that had been said and point the sisters in the direction of compromise. For three days she had struggled to achieve this.

Mother Leofric raised a hand; trusted Mother Leofric who had been given the headship of Perpetual Light on her recommendation, and could always be relied on to echo her ideas. She pointed gladly, willing Leofric to take over and bring the afternoon's debate to a close.

'As it is we wield little power,' Leofric said, then sat back silently.

Albergisten peered at her, and nodded her head waiting for her to continue, but the nun had said all she had to offer and could not be prevailed upon to add anything.

No one else attempted to speak. They sat around the table, their shoulders hunched, unable to agree.

'My sisters,' their superior said after some silence. 'Let us pray that God will show us his wish. We must pray for a miracle, we have no saints among us to add strength to our argument, we have none whose influence would save us. Let us pray that God will give us a sign.'

At this juncture, the abbess entered the room, and at once all heads turned to her out of relief. She bowed low and asked their forgiveness for her late arrival.

'Who is it? Who is it?' a blind nun asked of Mother Superior, who was already squinting to see.

Aelreda made her way to the top of the table for the customary blessing.

'We are glad to see you,' Mother Albergisten said and the young nun knelt to kiss her hand.

'Rise, my dear Sister in Christ.'

At the top of the table the nuns made room for the newcomer and each attempted by sign and gesture to nod their welcome to her.

'You are young,' Mother Superior addressed her. 'You will be among those left to carry on our work. I am old, and only hope that we survive. We have all spoken in turn. Some warn that survival might not be enough.' She looked chidingly towards the furthest end where Aelreda saw the huddle of nuns shaking their heads.

'I have noted it is those who shall continue the longest in this life who are more concerned not to assimilate. Therefore I, or rather we, cannot be hasty on any resolution. I understand that a command carried out in obedience rather than agreement will only make us discontented, and then, as a convent, what cause might overtake us? We need someone blest with divine sight, who can see a solution to this dilemma. What say you?'

Aelreda looked around. There was no straightforward resolution. Too many things were at stake and she saw that the nuns were tired. They wanted solace and they looked at her anxiously. She decided that her sisters needed strength and time to rest. They were weary of debating and wanted to feel they were united. Mother Albergisten was prepared to listen to ideas, she did not want to force the Rule's obedience as a way out of their locked position. What could she say to bring the meeting to a gentle finish before vespers?

'The power of prayer can never be understated,' she said. 'God will see to it that if we are intended to continue, we shall. If not, it is His will.'

She thought it was a weak attempt but it was wholeheartedly seized by the meeting.

'Well spoken Sister.'

The nuns nodded their heads in quick agreement, unanimous in their desire to call the end of session, and, stiff from sitting so long, they shifted and twisted causing benches to creak in approval.

Each nun hoped that a divine vision would be granted to their particular house, that in their midst a wonder-worker would be found, a nun of such sanctity that she could command emperors and popes by her communion with God. And they knew that they were unworthy to desire that such glory fall to them.

'Let us end here for private prayer and discussion,' Alber-gisten said, rising heavily and moving away so that the signal was given and all the nuns began to disperse, some silently, some in twos noisily, for permission had been granted and discussion was a pleasure.

Aelreda found herself with two who had eagerly taken up the debate. They walked abreast in the cloisters.

'A relic; we are short of relics. If only we had something priceless in our order which could be used to bless pilgrims with, then might we prosper and have a stronger case for remaining as we are.'

'The Grey Sisters at Auverne have the hand of Saint Menobh. And because of this they are able to host the annual pilgrimage on his feast day.'

'They make good use of such a holy relic. It is reputed to have performed a miracle on a blind man, restoring his sight after it was passed over his face. Their large convent in the south boasts the left hand also after his martyrdom.'

'I hear another convent boasts that they possess one of the same saint's hands.'

'That truly is miraculous.'

'If we could acquire such a relic we would be better positioned to argue for our own version of the Rule,' the thinnest nun said, and her eyes glowed strangely with desire.

But the others shrugged.

'We need to find a piece of the true cross at the very least and such things do not come easily. We would have to pay dear to own one. We do not have the means and we should need something startling – the bone of an apostle. But it would have to be a whole shin or a foot, not just a sliver. Just as a fragment of cloth from a saint's gown won't help us – we need the complete garment.'

'Yes, especially if it has blood stains from a martyrdom,' the thin sister added becoming more lively, 'or the cord which bound a martyred saint to the pillar before a disembowelling. The spilled guts in a casket would be good; all those little phials of blood could be sold. Or a painting that weeps or laughs.' Her hands twisted in excitement.

'But,' the other said, raising a hand to still her sister's energy, 'one order I have heard of does very well from tiny pieces of cloth which they have put in sealed glass containers with much ornamentation so that the casket which contains them is as worthy of a pilgrimage as the scraps of relic.'

'Ah, yes,' Aelreda agreed, 'but such works must take years to complete, a lifetime's work, and are they not costly?'

'Of course there are the Sisters of Compassionate Darkness.'

In the cloisters nuns gathered round.

'Oh, the Sisters of Compassionate Darkness.'

They took up the name like a litany, agreeing and falling into step behind each other. The abbess was puzzled.

'You would not be over familiar with them coming from so far north,' the thin sister explained. 'Their convent is high in the mountains. They are only a small order but have established for themselves a life of extreme privation cut off from all social intercourse. Yet they manage to be sufficient.'

Another cut in.

'Do you remember that terrible winter ten years previously? They had been depleted in dozens and the bishop himself travelled out to them as soon as the weather permitted and the pass was open again and he was horrified to see the fresh graves, which were shallow because the survivors had been unable to dig far below the frozen soil, being too weak. He moved the sickest into the hospice and tended to those close to death himself. Yet after the next synod no recommendations were enforced to make them ease their routine, although many were suggested.'

'Their individual character was left unchanged and they were able to continue as they always had, although they remained smaller in numbers.'

The abbess did not understand.

'How could this be?'

'You have not heard that they possess a remarkable relic?' the head of the newest house asked.

'They have such a relic! Oh, it is one the whole Christian world would cherish,' and she sighed with longing while her eyes closed.

'Yes, a relic that wars were fought for. Now it lies almost forgotten, high in the mountains, away from all the great institutions.'

Another nun, whose eyes narrowed as she spoke of holding such power, joined in: 'Think what that must feel like – when even the pope could not command its removal, nor expect to borrow it as he likes.'

'How is that?' The abbess was shocked.

'Because it has been decreed in a vision. That's how the home for the relic was chosen. There's no one can argue with that. And they keep hidden and silent, when they could exert such influence and be so wealthy. But the vision forbids it.'

The abbess still looked confused.

'I think I should explain,' Mother Superior said coming toward the group, 'as our young sister Aelreda has not heard tell of it.'

The nuns stood back respectfully as the old woman told again the story of how the relic was discovered. They all loved hearing it, every word was exactly as they knew it, for the story never wavered or altered, and they could have spoken it out loud as a chorus, ending on the same line, the same syllable. But they listened in respectful silence. The head of Crown of Thorns was a storyteller of some distinction.

As she spoke, Aelreda saw the scene unfolding as if she herself were present, as if she was the young maid in the legend. For so it ran: a young girl went wandering in the mountains after her father's goats which had gone far away from their usual spot. Following the sound of bleating she came to a place which she did not know. It was the furthest point before the forest began, thick and impenetrable. The young girl was hungry and thirsty, her legs were scratched and her feet bled from such a walk. In despair she buried her face in her hands. The two kids were nowhere in sight. The sound of wretched bleating echoed so that she could not tell from which direction it came.

The girl thought that she must have fallen asleep because when she lifted her head, instead of dusk it was as bright as day. She wondered if she had fainted and lain overnight. Yet she was not chilled, had no hunger and her feet were dry and clean as if they had been tended by someone.

Looking up, she saw a great lady dressed in delicate silks and carrying a circle of finely worked stones that sparkled like precious stars. The air was full of sweet perfume and in the distance she could hear the tinkling of bells.

The girl, in her ignorance, believed her to be a noble-woman who was lost and so she led the woman to safety and then went her own way home, thinking that she had been gone for many hours and would get a beating.

When she described her strange experience to her parents they laughed, for both goats had returned unharmed and the girl had been gone for such a short while that neither had missed her. They thought that she was playing games, but, being careful people, warned her not to speak of it to anyone, for there were others who might call her mad or possessed because of her fanciful imagination.

They thought no more about it, but the following night the girl saw the noble-woman again. She appeared in a dream, smiling her gratitude. She called the girl 'Daughter in Christ' and told her to dress and go quickly to the place where they had met. The girl woke, but she thought it was only a dream so she did not move but stayed, watching for the dawn.

For three nights she had the same dream. Each time she did nothing. Because of her parents' warning she told no one.

Upon the fourth night the woman appeared again. This time she cried and wrung her hands as she asked her why she would not do as she was bidden.

At this the young girl's heart flooded with compassion

and she rose quickly and was resolved to do exactly as the fine lady asked.

It was dark and the young maid stole out quietly, dreading that her parents should wake and scold her for her folly.

She walked to the place where, although it was night, the sun shone like day. There upon the ground lay a girdle, finely worked with beautiful silkwork such as she had never seen before, but a maternity girdle nonetheless, like the plainer one her own mother wore each time she was confined.

The young woman was terrified of what this meant, but heard a voice telling her to pick it up and take it with her. On her return the simple peasant hid the girdle, because she was scared if anyone found it they would say she had stolen it and her family would be brought into disgrace. She spoke to no one about it but the next night the lady appeared and said that she was pleased. She told the girl that she must take the girdle to a priest to be examined. So, the following day, she wrapped the object up in a worn blanket and, strapping it on her back, set out to walk to the village.

Her mother shouted at her because she was needed at home and her father struck her, yet the maid would not be dissuaded from her mission and asked them to forgive her, because she believed she would not see her parents again. When the sheriff discovered the wonderful piece of silkwork in her possession she was certain that she would be charged as a thief and not allowed to leave.

She went straight to the church and begged an audience with the priest, a kindly man they all said. She showed him the beautiful workmanship which she had concealed beneath an old blanket, in a bundle which made her look like a traveller on the road. After long examination the priest pronounced it the very same girdle of the Virgin, which had disappeared from Constantinople.

Asked how she had come by it the simple girl recounted her story and the good father understood at once that she had seen a vision of the Blessed Virgin. He humbly asked for her blessing, and the poor girl did not know how to make it, and the story is that she threw herself at his feet, crying and begging him not to mock her.

Mother Superior shook her head kindly, pausing in the telling. Several of the nuns wept with delight and blessed themselves.

'The girl was instructed by her vision,' Mother Superior continued, 'to establish an order of nuns at that spot in the mountains and dedicate her life to the service of the Heavenly Mother whose cherished girdle remains in their keeping.'

'Oh, yes, much money was raised from all the main religious orders, but a strange thing,' and the nun fixed the young abbess with a quizzical look. 'Instead of prospering, the order of Sisters of Compassionate Darkness has remained devoted to a life of poverty, for such had been the state of their foundress when she was shown favour by Our Lady.

'In poverty the Virgin lived, in poverty the Christ child was born. The girdle found a worthy home.' So ended Mother Albergisten.

All around heads nodded in time to the words. The abbess was crying as her head moved to the rhythm of the old nun's voice. In the chapel the bell rang for vespers. The nuns filed behind their superior.

Aelreda could not believe how quickly the evening came and throughout service she gave thanks for the beautiful story.

4

IRREGULAR HOUSES

THAT NIGHT AFTER COMPLINE, Aelreda knelt alone in the cell which had been made available to her. There was little difference between it and the one she occupied on her own site. Only the placing of the window, which here was high in the wall, while at Fortitude it came to her waist and afforded her a good view of the courtyard where she could watch the sisters crossing. This window showed only sky. It had two bars across the thick stone sides, and one heavy shutter had been thoughtfully closed half way so the night air might not chill the cell cruelly. A long rod with a hook lay propped against the wall. She hesitated for a minute, thinking to keep the room sharp, but instead took up the rod and pushed the shutters closed.

She prayed continuously, her thoughts fixed without deviation on the request for guidance, as a mind trained to focus can concentrate without interruption.

The hours passed quickly as she prayed, unaware in her dark cell of the night's speed. It was only when her head dropped with fatigue that in an attempt to keep vigil she opened the shutters wide and felt an icy rush of air which sharpened her senses. Then she noticed the creeping, grey light.

All night she thought about the marvellous story and saw the tableau unfolding vividly. It was as if the voice spoke to her in her sleep, telling her to build the foundations on the same site. Her mind dwelt upon the wonderful relic and the discussion she had had with the two nuns in the cloisters.

Buying relics was too costly a business for them to arrange. Their only chance would be to produce a visionary amongst them, one who heard the voice of God. Then they might have influence. But until such a miracle occurred, if it ever did, there was the question of their survival.

Aelreda worried. She doubted the sanctity of some of the work carried out by Scolastica, herbalist to her convent. She intended to seek advice from Mother Superior now that she was here. If there was any disturbance, any house showing unorthodox ways, it might cause an enquiry, then the order certainly could not hope to retain its independence. They would be swept along by the strongest current, pulled from their steady flow, to join, as a tributary swells the sea but is lost without the name of its river. They would become the next drowned souls.

The question over the time of inception, the point at which life is sanctified, troubled her. She was not a scholar of medicine and her reading, though sufficient, was not such that it had placed her early in a responsible post. That had been the result of her father's endowment to the foundation. She was not a theologian, no match for Scolastica, ill equipped to argue with any who could quote from Hippocrates and employ Aristotelian logic, or recite from Augustine's letters. Yet in her heart the abbess doubted the skills Scolastica practised, even while she could not put words to her ideas. And she dreaded that the whiff of heresy should be detected.

She was a practical woman, straight-thinking, unable to take her thoughts in leaps and bounds and connect several ideas at once, but she could focus on a point and reach some conclusion. As she prayed she wondered if they were to join themselves in some way to the Sisters of Compassionate Darkness, might it not be possible, by claiming allegiance with the order, to use some of the power the relic gave them to remain aloof from interference?

She was stiff with kneeling so long, and walked briskly

around her cell a few paces, then, crossing to the unslept-in bed, she took her small travel bag from where the lay sisters had deposited it earlier that day. She put her hand inside and felt around until she touched the hard leather handle and felt the tails of the small whip with their metal spikes. This she drew out, shuddering slightly. Pulling her robe over her shoulders to uncover her back, she stood upright and stiffened. Mouthing one of the psalms they would recite later that morning, she began working with the handle, at first softly, letting the little metal heads patter against her, then more rigorously until she felt at last the trickle of warm blood. Her arm slowed letting the whip tails sting into her hardened shoulders, which were thick with callouses and white scars.

'Dear Jesus, let me now atone for the luxury of flesh-meat and appetite which I enjoyed upon my journey. Let me make amends for every time my foul belly begged to be filled and I, weak sinner, gave in to it. No better than an animal I've been, sated, my guts heavy while in my province many starve.'

She dropped the discipliner out of her hand and stood with her arms outstretched in the shape of the crucifix, a position she would hold until the lay sister knocked the doors of the row to summon the nuns to matins.

In the dark, sisters shuffled in their night shoes towards choir; some were bleary, others eagle-eyed. Mouthing silent prayer they took up their positions. The visiting abbesses had a row of kneelers placed in front of the main choir and all the house waited until the guests were in place.

Aelreda felt healthy in spirit, and knew that she must seek an audience with Mother Superior that same day, for there was no time to hesitate or waver.

The Crown of Thorns convent was far larger than Fortitude, and not on a split site. Aelreda saw the choir with its row upon row of seats which was itself as large as their half side in church. There were over a hundred sisters gathered from all parts of Christendom.

A trained choir of nuns sang the Gregorian chants in a

way that the abbess had never heard or understood before, not one voice failing in the memorised notes, not one voice sinking beneath the rest, but a constant level of tone, a feat of great concentration. She wondered how many they knew by heart. At Fortitude they had lacked a music instructor since the death of Sister Saperid, and already the singing was becoming wavery, uncertain without the constant training. It was hard to master precise pitch and memorise the series of variations. She listened and was calmed.

After prime, as the congregation waited for first light in silent prayer, each internal voice pleaded for a miracle or, failing that, a solution. And Aelreda asked for two, like a greedy child.

Later that day before the first sitting of counsel the abbess requested an audience with Mother Albergisten and to her surprise was granted it immediately. The lay sister came almost at a run to the cloisters where she waited.

Mother Superior's apartments were sparse but comfortable, made so by the necessity of receiving visitors from outside. There were cushioned seats, and a heavy curtain to stop draughts hung on one wall in the antechamber where the lay sister left the abbess. On the opposite wall was a painting of a crucifixion scene, and next to this a depiction of Saint Veronica holding out the cloth with which she had wiped the face of Jesus. The abbess's eyes lingered hungrily on the images. In her own house there was nothing like this, no works of art nor even any wood carving. The face of the dying Christ pierced her heart and tears quickly came. Such love as she bore for the Son of God was overwhelming and she gazed into the painted eyes while her own brimmed and the figure blurred in front of her. Her breathing became slower and was very deep. Her legs crumpled under her. She caught the edge of the kneeler for support.

'Sister in Christ, dearest Aelreda! You are weak and have gone without sleep I see!'

Mother Superior's voice took her unawares as she came up behind her.

'At my time of life, I feel it is necessary to sleep when the order permits it, ah, those long nights of prayer of my youth are gone now,' she said wistfully.

'But sit now, and rest yourself.'

Then the older woman looked stern.

'I pray that tonight you will not attempt to deprive yourself again, we need clear heads for this debate.'

'I will obey whatever you ask of me,' the abbess replied, taking the proffered hand and kneeling to kiss the ring.

'Well, well . . . Sit, dear Sister, I will not allow my nuns to drive themselves too hard. You request an audience, and I am sure that you have something pressing to ask of me. Continue, and do not be at a loss for words. Whatever you say is between we two alone. Have you doubt? Is it a spiritual matter?'

The old nun went easily into her role of confessor and confidant.

'It is not my faith which I doubt, Mother. But I am greatly troubled about irregularities,' Aelreda began. 'In my own house there is Scolastica, a wise elder, who practises the art of medicine in a way which I now have grave cause to question.'

'My sister in God,' Mother Albergisten said shaking her head, 'I think, as you are so far removed from the rest of our branches, you indeed might have grown further from the root. Are you committed to the Rule as it was written by Benedict?'

'Yes Mother.'

'Then what irregularities can there be, if you keep to the Rule as it has been ordained?' The old nun looked kindly at the young abbess. 'I see that you are striving hard, maybe too hard, to be a perfect copy of the other houses, but,' and she looked around beckoning for silence, then continued with a lowered voice, 'there are such things in many houses as would make you deny them.'

She tapped the crucifix about her neck with her index finger.

'Mother, what can you mean by this?' the abbess asked.

Mother Albergisten raised her eyebrows and looked quizzically at her.

'It is well known that you dislike the policy of accepting those of small vocation but of great dowry.'

The abbess blushed.

'It is to your credit that this system finds distaste with you.'

It was more than distaste. The abbess found, when driven to accept such entrants through financial necessity, despite the massive influx of wealth, that the dissatisfaction of the charges soon spread into the rest of the convent. The more worldly nuns became aggrieved when they saw these nuns set up in separate quarters with their own female servants who would perform the eight hours of labour each was expected to contribute daily to the order.

They brought with them furnishings and fabrics to make their cells more than comfortable and even had their own versions of the habit, with a variety of becoming head-dresses. They were the rich daughters who for one reason or another could not be bought suitable marriage partners and so were forced into religious life. Many of them were kept hidden; vain foolish girls who could not work and languished in the community.

Mother Albergisten knew this problem well. She had faced the same difficulties throughout her time as head of a smaller house in the west. Despite coming from well-connected families, their education was often lacking and they were fed on fantasies, unable to stick long enough at anything to develop an interest in it, like butterflies they skitted from one occupation to the next, eternally bored and joyless.

Some managed better than others, even began to adapt to the Rule and lived it in a reduced manner. Those who had a modicum of education, enough to be able to read, could spend time studying the books in the library and be trained as inkers in the scriptorium. But it was awful to see some of the young entrants pining, still believing that after a spell in the convent their fathers or guardians would come for them. It took years before they understood that vows taken unwillingly or as a game were just as binding.

Cut off from everything they had known these sisters faded away, refusing food. On many occasions Mother Albergisten had been called to intervene when one was close to death. As it was they made every provision they could for these gilded ones to pass their time easily, removed from the routine of the convent proper. They even allowed them access to the outside on those sites where the lay sisters were not enclosed. It was difficult if a guardian expressly forbade this, then there might be little respite for the novice from the everyday life of the convent. Even if they took no part in it, it was all around them, dampening their sensual appetites with frugality. Many wasted and died as the iron-worded vows ensured that for the rest of their mortal days they would live as nuns.

Aelreda had seen in her own house how, unaccustomed to hardship, these gilded sisters became the first to suffer from the ravages of the famine which had afflicted the regions for almost a year.

'We buried five last winter. I cannot commit my nuns to any more. But those who are still with us have adapted, making obedient sisters.'

Mother Superior smiled, remembering how the abbess herself was presented to them as the child of wealthy patrons.

'But are these the irregularities you wish to speak of? My dear child in God, there are many far greater. Do you not know of the orchard and cider presses at Perpetual Light which made that house the most prosperous business in their area? And we need that revenue. The food at Bleeding Lance they say, makes even fast days look like feasts. Poor Sister Corpulus!'

Mother Superior laughed, imagining the portly head of Bleeding Lance.

'She had been here but a week when we found her trying to

bribe the lay sisters in the kitchen to bring a bowl of vegetable stew to her cell.'

She laughed again and shook her head like a fond parent contemplating a wayward, but much loved child.

'She has a belly unused to fasting, and here our resources are stretched, with the extra mouths to feed. She begged pardon, as guilty as if she had sinned against God. But the Good Lord knows her weakness, and if he is tolerant of it, why should we not be here? And as for your gilded sisters, there are worse ways of treating them than to keep them in luxury. In some houses chains are used. One house has four who regularly must be restrained. They keep them out of sight, tethered as beasts. Do you think this is a better way to treat them?'

The elderly nun spread herself comfortably on the cushioned seat.

'Is it true that in some houses the punishment is never taken?' asked the abbess.

'My dear,' Albergisten replied kindly, 'in some houses I suspect that the life might even suit your own gilded sisters. And there are irregularities we must clear up – we will be seen to be correct and proper in all our doings. We will tighten up our days so that not one thought can be spent in idleness, not one thought lost in dreaming. Then what can we fear, if we are seen to obey?'

Aelreda had dedicated her house to chastity and the easing of those fallen. Yet she had a distaste for the physical. She only imagined what it could be. She had seen desperate women arriving at the turn-gate, wretched beyond all hope, they came to be purged of their grossest activity. She could not understand why any of them should suffer so for their actions.

She suspected that the purgings were not always accurate and it disturbed her. When it was inappropriate, some women stayed their time in the infirmary.

'It is a theological matter which disturbs me, a point upon which I need correction,' she said after some silence. Cider presses and robes made of silk were nothing compared to her anxieties. She tried as best she could to put her fears into words. But she was faltering and even in the discussion with Mother Albergisten, who knew nothing of the practices and writings of Scolastica, she felt that she could not describe the link between practice and belief.

'You keep a convent dedicated to God. You are severe on yourself. If you pray, God will answer,' her superior said, moving the audience to an end. She was a busy woman.

'And now we must rejoin the others for the debate will shortly be called to session. Tell me,' she enquired, 'have you had any further thoughts on the matter?'

Aelreda knew that she had not expressed her worry, but Mother Albergisten wanted to round it off and get back to the overriding problems of their order. Now she wondered if she worried unduly; there were other pressing matters at hand. She could not voice her difficulties. Instead in answer she began to discuss her idea for claiming allegiance to the Sisters of Compassionate Darkness.

'I hoped that if it were possible we might then be able to share the privilege that such a relic affords. Surely when these sisters are made aware of our plight they will help us out of charity?'

'Yes,' the old nun said, 'I shall put that to counsel. Although it might mean a much harder Rule for many, and that will not be popular. Let us walk together to the chapter house.'

For the first time the young abbess felt that she was not misplaced as head of a convent. She might allow herself the sin of pride. She had one of the most orderly houses. She could not prevent a half smile of satisfaction as she entered behind Mother Superior and the assembly rose.

'Sisters, let us reconvene and first offer a prayer that we find a solution to our problems.'

The abbess stared past the reader and thought about the Sisters of Compassionate Darkness. Without some alliance their order would not survive. They would vanish like so many small orders had already.

'It is God's will, if we are to survive or not,' a nun said.

Then let us know soon, the abbess thought, for she knew that outside of the order there was nothing.

PART TWO

STRAINING THE
EYES

5

THE CONVENT OF THE
SILENT MARTYRHOOD

Sister Cecile winced at the deafening noise which announced the end of class. It was a new sound. The workmen who installed the mechanism were still dropping bits of multi-coloured flex in the yard when the autumn term started. Although the electronic timer could never go unheard and was more accurate, Cecile preferred the hand held bells which monitors rang haphazardly in corridors. She missed the carillon from uncoordinated doorways as each class realised it was running late.

She watched the navy-blue line of twitching gymslips, relieved as the last one went through the door. Everything seemed louder this term. The girls had changed; inspired by the new bells they became rowdy and the first-years seemed brasher than ever.

Reverend Mother had eased Cecile's teaching load this term; a semi-retirement because she was sixty-five. That burned in her mind. Last week they celebrated her birthday with a special early mass and in the evening Sister Benedict brought her a plant from the conservatory, a small shoot which she had tended and re-potted to give her. They decided that it should be placed in the doorway to the main building.

'It's your plant Sister. That means no one else will water it,' and they had all laughed in the common room.

There was a special treat for tea as there was when any of the sisters' birthdays fell on clear days. Those with the misfortune to be born on a day of obligation or during Lent could count on nothing to mark the routine fasting. That evening it had still been the same plain meal, and Cecile wondered if there would be an extra slice of bread, perhaps a different type of cheese. It had been a small gooseberry tart which they divided up.

On her birthday she always thought of her great-aunt who lived to be ninety-eight. Longevity pleased her. Her mother's side boasted numerous figures who lasted well into their nineties. It was not pride, for that would not have been proper, but she drew strength from the idea that she might follow suit. To steal another thirty years and to write the history book she had wanted to since she gained her M.A. forty years ago.

She had wanted to study for her Ph.D. but Reverend Mother would not give her permission, nor would she give in to pressure by the university. A tutor came out to the convent to argue with her, describing Cecile as potentially one of the best medievalists in the country, someone who ought to spend time in research. Not once did he suggest to Cecile that she ought to think again about her chosen life, or hint that the discipline of the convent was wrong for her. She alone asked herself that when the argument still raged.

Now she was too old to consider any changes in her life. She sat back on the wooden seat and took out of her briefcase the copy of a document that had arrived that morning from the Historical Society. She had fifteen minutes before the bell and she intended to use them.

She began reading the first line, savouring the cadence of the Latin prose, and was sucked into the text.

When she had been working for her M.A. she had examined original manuscripts. That had been her peak, never to be experienced again. But even with copies she could become dead to the present as the hand of the scribe beckoned her into another experience, buried deep within an illumination. She would lose herself inside the maze of a letter, follow animals into another time as they twisted the loops of a capital. Eyes watched from the page, a scribe's pen could be felt tracing words. Sometimes she imagined the slow speaking voice of a long-dead reader, and she wondered how they might have struggled with the Latin syntax, so different from their own, as they gave the lesson in a cold, dust-blown refectory.

In these pages were souls eager to be discovered. If they could pull her hand, guide her eyes, how greater would her understanding be. She would appeal to them. Pray that she might discover their lives, and offer blessings for them. But sometimes a character leapt from a page, defiant and angry at being disturbed. Then she knew she touched the soul of one condemned for eternity.

Now as she read along the second line of the copy she was aware of someone breathing. She heard a cough and knew she was being watched.

She raised her head and saw black shoes, grey tights and the navy gymslip of the convent school. A small dark girl stood waiting, the collar of her blouse worn and the top button undone visibly beneath the blue and grey striped tie.

'Well?' Cecile asked.

'Sister?'

The girl shifted her weight from foot to foot. Cecile hated when people did not come straight to the point.

'Come on, come on!' she snapped irritably, her reading time interrupted. 'What do you want girl, don't stand gawking.'

'You told me yesterday to see you after first session this morning.'

Cecile stared at the girl. She could not give her a name.

'About my essay,' the girl volunteered.

Of course. She had forgotten. This was the girl who had sent in the ridiculous homework.

Cecile lifted the heavy desk lid and pulled out the buff copy book. 'Siobhan Doolin. Lower-sixth arts' was written on the cover in the neat square hand Cecile recognised as late adolescent. A few years out of school, working or studying under pressure, and the writing cracked. Occasionally, in exam years the handwriting became an adult scrawl with no concern for neatness or legibility. She had one such paper returned last summer by the chief examiner because no one could read it.

She looked at the characters on the copy book. They were still in that happy stage when the penmanship lessons of primary school held good, and the letters were plain and clear. Her own writing had become illegible. It frustrated her when after making notes she found that she could not read them. If only she had the discipline of the medieval scribes who kept all individualism out of their work and followed an exact method, although now and again a blast of something different was added in the margins as the scribe put comments, even the odd little joke, in a faster, urgent hand. But then writing was an art, not solely a means to an end.

'I have not had the misfortune to teach you before. I presume that you followed the history course throughout lower school and passed well at "O" level to be in this option group now?' she said.

The girl nodded.

'Let me remind you that this is not an easy option, and if, for whatever reason, a pupil can't manage the course, I can recommend their removal into Modern History with Sister Joseph.'

'Yes Sister,' the girl said and looked down.

Cecile turned the page of the book and read the essay question. It had been neatly written and underlined. 'Examine the influence of Columba's settlement on the development of the pre-Norman church.'

She turned towards the girl.

'Tell me,' she said, 'do you think you've answered this?'

The girl looked confused but said nothing.

'You were supposed to discuss the pre-Norman church showing which developments of the Irish monastic movement in Gaul were absorbed. Could you give me an example now of something that links the growth of monasticism with Columba's influence? What for example were the Irish monks famous for?'

Cecile wanted to sort out quickly those who had an aptitude. This girl had the air of fatality about her. Let Sister Joseph take her on so that she could concentrate on the brighter ones.

'What were the Irish monks famous for?' she repeated carefully and waited. Now she had her. The girl looked uneasy.

'For the introduction of private penance, Sister,' she said. 'So that confession became an individual rather than a public sacrament.'

Cecile was surprised.

'So you do know something. But why did you send in homework that told a story about sea-travel, about visions due to lack of clean drinking-water? You sent in an account that would do justice to a science-fiction comic. Tell me, do you watch much television?'

'No Sister.'

'Then why this homework?' She felt confused.

'It's the influence, Sister,' the girl said.

'Explain?'

'I wanted to write about those ... feelings, which made people give up everything. To go off, not knowing what they'd find, not even knowing if they'd survive the journey. They must have felt their faith that strongly ... well, I thought that was the best example of Columba's influence.'

'It was not what I asked you to do,' Cecile remarked drily. 'Did you trouble to read the work I recommended?'

'Yes Sister. How else could I have known about the monks having visions?'

'You have obviously read the book. Possibly you've spent too long on chapters that are not relevant to this essay. Didn't I give you the page numbers?'

The girl nodded.

'Then I suggest that you stick to them.'

'Yes Sister.' Again, the girl stared at her feet.

'You'll have to repeat this homework. Pay proper attention to the reference material.'

She shut the copy book and handed it back across the gulf of desk.

'You may go.'

The girl turned, but at the door Cecile called her.

'Siobhan Doolin.'

'Yes Sister?'

'It is necessary to stick to the facts, as we find them. That is how we look at history. Facts. Without them we can prove nothing.'

'Yes Sister.'

After the girl left, Cecile wondered what facts really were. The girl had been more right than she knew. No doubt she watched too much rubbish on TV and had an over-active imagination. No doubt she was lazy, too lazy to pay attention to the question, yet she had fallen into the spirit of the age by accident. Cecile was surprised by the underlying veracity; even something as great as the Benedictine order had its foundations in a simple ideal, in a feeling from the heart, not in decrees and great power or control. No, the starting points were all the mad men in the sun, those desert fathers and pillarists, the strange, demented visionaries who were laughed at. But her duty as a teacher was to get girls through the 'A' Level. This would not.

But what were facts? Their own Saint Polycarp had the legend that at his martyrdom, as the torturers pierced his side, a white dove flew out. To whoever wrote the tale up, that event was real; a dove might fly from a man's side. A white dove, the old symbol for the soul, its purity and its flight heavenwards to God in times when flight was still miraculous. Cecile understood the allegory. It was her work to understand, yet there were nuns in the convent who taught that story as fact and girls who believed it as such.

That girl's young mind had touched something. It made Cecile sad because her own was in decay. She was in a race against time to keep her clarity.

The bell rang and the sound of footsteps echoed down the wooden corridor as the girls came back to their classrooms in ranks. She had to teach the first year religious instruction then she had a half hour session with the fourth form all before lunch. As she put the text back into her bag she realised that she had barely read any of it.

That evening after supper Sister Cecile walked back to the school building to work in her study, which was also the stockroom for the history department. It was not warm as she crossed the gardens so she wore her shawl and moved quickly. If she kept her head bent she might appear devout. Anyone would think she was praying and not disturb her.

She seldom got time alone to think. She disliked interruptions and had to train herself not to feel angry when suddenly asked a question while deep in thought. She was not a dreamer. If anything she was the opposite. She believed she had no imagination. She was always trying to connect facts and make links between what she read and what she felt, but she did it by the study of recorded details, proven theories. She thought about the girl's essay. There was something in it that always evaded her, it was the smell of life rather than of death.

All day she repeated to herself what she told the girl; that it was necessary to stick to the facts. But when she thought about how information was stored and selected she felt less confident. Who decided what was worthy of preserving, who decided what was worthy of attention, which tale to tell? And she began to wonder, because the girl's homework had disturbed her. What did they see when they hallucinated? What made them go so gladly into a dangerous venture, swept along by religious fervour until they became oblivious to their own safety? With a cold feeling she realised then that whatever it was, she had never experienced it.

What had prompted her to give up her life outside? Something had moved her, love of God, of duty perhaps, but not wildness, never a passion. Into her rusted memory she locked phrases and feelings that no longer belonged to her. She wanted ecstasy. That was the promise of her calling. Instead she found drudgery.

By the greenhouse two lay sisters were digging. They wore grey wellingtons and had tucked up the front of their habits inside the large pockets of their heavy underskirts. Those pockets were a godsend. Cecile always kept chalk and a duster in them. Sister Ignatius made her laugh once by pulling a pair of secateurs from hers.

A few years ago the order had relaxed its rule on silence. Now some conversation was allowed during work periods. The two nuns were talking as they pulled up winter cabbage, tossing the small dark knots of vegetable into a basket. They wore rubber gloves. In her day that would not have been allowed; they would have been told to offer up the discomfort to God. Things were changing. As she passed they fell silent and stopped working, bowing stiffly from the waist to greet her deferentially. Her seniority and her profession meant that they must remain silent until she passed. It was the order of things.

She went in through the side door and walked up the sweeping central flight of stairs, crossed the mezzanine with the portrait of their founder, and continued up a narrow unvarnished course of stairs that went up to the various rooms. At the very top she stopped for breath, leaning on the banister. She noticed of late that she had a tendency to become giddy. But this last flight was especially steep and winding so it was not surprising that it should make her pant.

On one dreadful occasion she had misplaced her footing and caught the narrowest point of the step and, as her foot floundered, she fell and slid the length of the splintery wooden steps on to the first platform which mercifully broke her fall. Her stockings were laddered and the skin on both knees had broken in grazes which stung for days after.

A fall like that left her in doubt. Any sign of physical frailty made her nervous that she might not have all the

time she hoped for. She was grateful that she had fallen
during a free lesson when she ought to have been marking
exercise books, and not during lunch-break or mid-morning
recess when some of the pupils were bound to be prowling
the lower corridors. They would have caught her and fussed,
as shocked as the victim; but later the fall would have become
an event. The Day Sister Cecile Fell Down The Stairs would
pass into the school's history. She dreaded any fuss. If she
became breathless she preferred to stand still, to bend her
head and breathe deeply. Anyone seeing her might think she
was praying, yet in her quiet moments she did not pray. She
thought of all manner of things: the history book, her health,
her family. Somehow God had been pushed to the edges.

At the top of the landing was the cubby hole where books
were kept. She had the key to it on a long silver chain about
her waist together with a heavy black and silver crucifix, a
small paper-knife and a propelling pencil in a case, like a
medieval housewife keeping her salt, knife and vital tools about
her. These were the tokens of her work. Anyone could tell that
she was a teaching nun; her bony fingers were always dusty
from writing on blackboards and in the sleeves of her habit she
tucked small pieces of chalk, rolling up one arm band higher
than the other.

As a figure she was gaunt and sinewy. Beneath the hem
of her skirt the bones of her ankles stuck out. Skinny was a
new word and too crude for her vocabulary, but she thought
of it and laughed; it was how the girls described her. The tight
fitting hood about her face hid her thin neck to the world, but
it had tendons like harp strings. She could feel them when she
washed, could have played on them, plucking a tune from their
sunken folds. Her body withered. Strange to think that while
they ate the same food, fasted at the same time, some sisters
grew fat and rounded while others shrivelled with the life.

Under her head-dress her close cropped hair was dark grey
turning lighter and more colourless. Sometimes she would see
the ends lying on the floor after the three-monthly cut with

Sister Gabriel wielding the scissors in the passage. She did not think about it, she had never suffered for vanity, even during the brief part of her life which she had spent outside.

She took the heavy key up in her right hand and struggled with the stiff lock. The wooden door creaked open and she went into her private domain.

She was not supposed to feel that it was her place, but once here she could shut the door and be undisturbed. It was a tendency she had to want to be on her own and not always 'in common'. To stop this, she had taken to leaving the stock-room door wide open as a penance for her selfish desires. But it was still her place, because at the top of the stairs she could hear anyone approach. She could differentiate the sounds. She knew if it was a sister or a pupil, or one of the lay teachers in their funny little shoes that clattered so horribly on the stairs. She had time to be ready for the intrusion with good grace or a stern word if it was one of the sillier pupils.

Reverend Mother had insisted that she take up a hobby during the one hour a day they kept for recreation. Cecile had been distraught, her life was history. She wanted that hour to put towards research. She had asked the head to reconsider.

'You must take part in some other activity Sister,' she had said. 'It is an order that you undertake recreation willingly for the love of God, in humility.'

She went as far as to suggest that Cecile take up a musical instrument. At her age! One hour a week. She wondered if her superior wanted her to look silly as she struggled, while Reverend Mother who had trained as a cellist in her youth, would preen.

She quashed the thought, not wanting to doubt the other's motives, but had side-stepped neatly, saying that she would do some embroidery, and for one hour a week she watched a tablecloth with scalloped edges of poppies take shape before her. It might have been relaxing if she could have been certain that she would have enough time left. She wanted to live to see her book complete. She tried adding up the hours of free time she might expect to have: she would have to live for at least thirty years in order to get as much as she needed, and that was assuming her mind was going to be clear towards the end. Each time she raised the matter she had been made to reread the lesson on humility. If she was fortunate to have a gift from God, she was not going to be allowed to use it.

She did not argue, but made peace with God and prayed for forgiveness for her wicked thought. Reverend Mother was wiser. But still, she thought she was envious. Quickly she took down a stack of books and started to count them, putting everything out of her mind except the droning of numbers as she noted the batches in her account book.

Outside it darkened. Quickly the late September sky changed. She worked on unaware. Into each book she pasted a white, paper label which would be filled in with the year and the name of each student who used the book, so that they could be checked in the holidays and made ready for the next influx of students.

She sat hunched over the small desk top, gumming into frontispieces the white squares with the school's crest, a soaring dove that flew above the empty lines.

She glanced up and saw a face. She started, not recognising who it was that looked at her so intently. The small window over the desk was black-mirrored to the sky. Cecile turned away, making the sign of the cross for the accidental act of vanity, but, as she worked on, her head kept lifting to watch the stranger in the glass. She looked older than she thought she might, more like her mother than she could believe. But the reflected face was older than the weeping woman who would not say goodbye. Cecile left the family house for good and her mother remained locked in her room. As the black taxi drove off Cecile looked up to catch her mother's face, hard at an upstairs window.

'Mother,' Cecile said aloud in the stockroom and was shamed by the memory as much as by her compulsion to look. They were to put their pasts behind them and their lives were to begin again as Brides of Christ – one day old in a mystic marriage – the day they became members of the community.

She had not expected her face to be so sunken. She turned her head to one side to see her profile, praying to God to forgive her. She felt the ridge of her nose, straight and sharp. A mean nose.

When she was a girl her hair used to be black and she had thick, dark eyebrows. At least they still seemed dark but they were unkempt and ungroomed. Around her lip the dark moustache she used to pluck out as a young woman now mocked her womanhood. She laughed at her embarrassment and as she did she saw the large teeth, long where the gums had receded. She was no beauty. She laughed again. She had meant it as a statement of fact; there was no tinge of regret, nor even value in the word 'beauty'.

She knew that the good Lord would see that her heart was free from vanity yet she put her hand up and set her wimple straight. She had walked around all day like that and no one had said anything to her. Despite everything it vexed her, even as she got up from the table to move away from the temptation to sin. She took all the remaining books into another corner and for the next hour continued working without another glance at the window.

That night as she prepared for sleep she realised that she had forfeited all her time to read during the day and soon the light would be out. She would lie still, feigning sleep. If only she could use that extra waking hour for study, but that was just a vain dream of hers for more time.

Along the row Sister Martin was coughing. Cecile hung her veil and turned her habit inside out upon her hanger in the large wardrobe at the end of the corridor. She removed the white starched wimple and put it in the linen basket by the main door. New ones had already been placed in the wardrobe by the laundry nuns. One of them, Sister Gertrude, was a member of this passage. She had worked in the laundry since joining the order eighteen years ago. It was a mystery to Cecile how they made the fronts so stiff. They wore them under the little poke-bonnets which dated back to their foundress in the seventeenth-century and had never been altered. They blinkered them at the sides with the crisp folds worn tightly against the face. At first it had been a penance but now Cecile felt uncomfortable without it, as if her head might turn on a swivel and she would see in all directions at once.

She stroked her grey hair and at the same time noticed how Sister Gertrude watched her. That look would mean a warning from Reverend Mother at breakfast. Walking slowly back to her cell she sat and removed her thick stockings, and hung them neatly over the back of the chair. The order believed in modesty, not humiliation. She shut the door and finished undressing, putting on the heavy cotton shift they all wore at night. She reached for the hairnet. Wonderful things, they had been brought in a few years earlier when it was found that the wearing of one meant less time was needed combing. Her own hair was about four inches long, growing out from the last cut. Many of the nuns kept theirs quite long under their head-dresses. It was a matter of what cost the least time; if the wimple fitted neatly the rest of the hair was forgotten.

When Cecile first came to the order girls wore their plaits very long; short hair was like a punishment and she did not forget how it felt to see her plait lie on the floor. Now it was not the least emotive. Girls coming in already had shorter hair than the sisters. Horrified, she realised that as she was thinking she rubbed her head automatically. She snatched her hand away.

'Forgive me Jesus,' she prayed and lay down folding her arms across her chest in the manner of the angels.

That night she focused on Mary's sorrows at the cross as her last thoughts. She said three extra decades of the rosary, forcing her eyes open until she finished. Despite this precaution, it was her face and her mother's from long ago which were her last thoughts as she drifted into sleep.

6

DISCOVERY

WINTER CAME FORWARD QUICKLY. The term was short, the lessons rapid, and the bell deafening.

Cecile remarked one morning to Sister Joseph in the common room that she had been surprised by one of her pupils.

'She has quite a grasp of the period. I think she ought to do well, if she continues to work at the same rate. She's made such progress after a shaky start.'

'That's the problem with adolescent girls. They fall in love with some boy and the next thing you know you've lost them. I'd never go through that agony again. I think it's the most awful stage in anyone's life, that middle period when they're not yet adults but no longer children. I went through agonies . . .'

'You sister?' Cecile was laughing now.

'Of course.' She sounded indignant at the surprise in Cecile's voice. 'Didn't you? I was wild for some film actor. I forget his name now. Thank the Lord it's all over. I'm a calm woman given to contemplation. Like most of these will be when they get a bit older. Education is all the wrong way round.' She shook her head slowly from side to side. 'They'd benefit from it in a few years' time, after all this romantic stuff is out of their systems. If only we could drop them for a couple of years then pick them up again,' and, lifting an armful of exercise books from the cupboard, she strode off to her next lesson.

Cecile watched her, staid Sister Joseph who had once been wild for a film actor. What must she have been like then, before she grew into the efficient, black-robed figure who swept silently along corridors? An admission of girlhood from any of the sisters was always a shock. It was an owning up to a previous identity. A crush on a film actor – impossible! Cecile smiled at the improbability of it, but when she thought about herself (and she knew she wasn't supposed to dwell on memories) there was nothing to shock, to throw out of joint the image of herself. At sixteen she was a serious girl, only interested in school.

Her father expected great things from her. She was the eldest of his three girls. Had there been sons the expectations might not have been so pressing, but both parents looked to her to set the tone. It was academic, the route she chose, and it would have continued to be so if not for the abrupt way she had learned about life.

She tried to remember herself, was she ever a laughing girl, a dreamer? The description did not fit. She had been a respectable girl. The word rose up as if from an acid stomach. Her throat gagged. Respectability was what she strove for, what her mother believed in.

It was wrong to wallow in memory; the past was too often an excuse for pride. But this order did not erase her girlhood. That was impossible to accomplish. To forget everything when she could still smell how the air changed by the stables at home, still reel off the list of ancestors. She came from a good family. The thought was there before she could suppress it. Her mother always said that she could be proud of her name.

And now it was too late, the entire memory played back the way it did occasionally, whenever her energy was low, or her resolve weak. It still made her angry.

She was seventeen, running shoeless down the great staircase holding up her skirt so that she could go faster. She did not care what she looked like, who saw her stockings. The stable-hand looked away. She rushed past him, would have knocked him down to get to where her father lay, stretched out on the sofa where the men had laid him. It had been one of his favourite horses, that made it worse. She hated horses after that. Could never go near them. They thought that the end of the world had come. Their mother was helpless with grief. But it was only the beginning.

After the funeral a letter. A woman who called herself his wife in everything but law wanted to know if payments would be kept up, on account of the child. She cried for days. Her two sisters walked the grounds in stunned silence.

It was their mother's brother who made all the financial arrangements. He gave instructions for money to be paid from their father's estate. 'It's what he would have wanted.'

But their mother believed she was eternally wronged. To have found out in such a way. She said the woman was bleeding them dry, taking everything from his legitimate descendants. That became her stock phrase.

'No matter what anyone says, you are the legitimate descendants. There is no stain on any of you, or on myself. We are the proper family.'

She remembered seeing the original letter. The address in a part of town she was not familiar with.

'But how could they have ever met?' she asked. Then something about the way her mother froze and her uncle looked away made her regret the naïve question. Later she understood, but at seventeen she was still learning the ways of men and women.

How she used to hate her then, this woman she was never to meet. She imagined her, a red-faced, coarse creature with short hair and a fringe, so unlike her mother – a sensitive woman with pale skin who wore her long, dark tresses in a knot.

When she understood, she blamed this other for sucking her father into depravity. It was revolting how she must have baited their father with sex. The dreaded word. The promise of it hung about this woman. Their house promised cold respectability.

And she wondered what it must be like if it was able to wreck lives and make people behave wildly. Would she ever feel something so powerful that she would be lost to reason? She doubted it, but yearned to. Her father took the route that turned men into animals, leaving a trail of shame and anguish behind. Their mother was always devout. She said pure love was spiritual. But not if it meant losing the eldest daughter.

Reverend Mother was calling her name. Cecile felt annoyed. It was the anniversary of their convent. Two hundred and fifty years the Silent Martyrhood had been established in this building. The newest in the order. A massive event was being planned. She knew that Reverend Mother wanted to check up to see how far she had got with the arrangements for the historical pageant. The celebrations were not for months. Why was Reverend Mother so agitated? Then she saw that she waved a manilla envelope at her. She was grinning.

'Sister,' she drew Cecile inside her office. 'Such news! The governors have agreed to put up the money for the restoration work that is needed!'

Cecile gasped. Maybe now something could be done about the library and her precious books.

'And so I have decided to engage workers to paint and renovate the chapel.'

Cecile managed to nod.

'Yes, Reverend Mother, that is a good idea, although I had hoped that something could be done about the library.'

'I am aware of the deteriorating state of the library, but the roof of the chapel is becoming dangerous. I must consider it first.'

Reverend Mother drew away from her and stood by her desk. She put the envelope down and looked at it for a moment in silence.

'But I have something to tell you, which should be of special interest ... an art expert from the city gallery is coming out to have a look at the altar piece ... at the central panel which you have always said is older than we believe. He comes primarily to restore it so that it will not deteriorate further. The chapel will be renovated in the summer holidays during recess, but the restorer wants to look at the painting immediately. He wrote to arrange a time to come and see it. Time, it seems, is of the essence in these matters. He may have to begin work on it quickly. Damp might make it beyond repair by summer.'

'Reverend Mother, why are you telling me this?'

'Because it was your anxiety about damp ruining the books that prompted me to act, to write to various bodies and commissions to see what could be done, so your efforts were not all in vain. We will be able to see our blessed Saint Polycarp in all his glory as the painter intended. And it will please the governors no end. If there is any money remaining, the library is to be treated.'

Cecile could not suppress her delight.

'That is wonderful news!' she exclaimed.

'This letter,' the nun continued, 'from the restorer . . . I wondered if you might like to be involved in it, if you can agree a time for the expert to come out and discuss it with him . . . I expect he will decide which course to take. And I can arrange for you to be released from lower-school teaching. Tell me Sister, does that sound agreeable to you?'

'Yes Reverend Mother. Very agreeable. Only . . . well, if I could have the extra hour that is made available for recreation . . .'

'I'm afraid that is impossible.' The other nun straightened up, all the warmth gone from her voice.

'Of course,' Cecile said. 'I only meant to enquire.'

Handing over the letter Reverend Mother terminated the discussion with a hope that it would not be too much responsibility.

'No, Reverend Mother. Thank you,' Cecile said, and her thanks were sincere.

A fortnight after her conversation with Reverend Mother the restorer arrived. It caused some excitement in the school especially with the younger girls who were fascinated by the fact of the worker's maleness. Cecile used to wonder at it. Let any man set foot inside the school buildings and the girls seemed to quiver with excitement, strange looks came over their faces and they simpered, walking along the corridors, swinging their hips from side to side. But it disturbed the convent too. Cecile noticed that there was an awkwardness about the sisters when men were on the premises. Maybe if they took on male members of staff it would relieve the tension in the school, but it would not be a popular move, and it would not alter anything for the lay sisters who, apart from the convent chaplain who said mass for them, never dealt with men.

The restorer had arrived early on Monday. She did not know how long he must have waited in the convent garden because the doorkeeper that day was Sister Benedict, notorious for not hearing the bell and never hurrying when she did.

Cecile however almost ran to the waiting room when she was told that the 'restorer gent' had arrived.

When she saw him, she was disappointed. He was too young, surely? She felt nervous. His authority vanished with his years. In his letter he had sounded knowledgeable. It was hard not to feel let down. He carried no briefcase but instead a curiously worn suitcase of quite a small size. His hair was unkempt and he sported an awful beard. Cecile was ever wary of beards. They hid the chin, and you could never be sure about a fellow's character without a chin. His teeth were over-large, best suited to smiling because when he did not smile his mouth looked stretched over them as if he was about to ask a question. When he smiled his face relaxed.

As soon as she entered the room he was on his feet. Small and eager, he held out a hand.

'Sister Cecile Dyson?'

'You must be Mr Wainsworth?'

'Alan Wainsworth, yes. I'm delighted to meet you at last.'

He was over-thin, she decided. Probably lived in a bed-sit and ate everything out of tins. His wrists were too narrow for his shirt cuffs. Terrible jacket. But his hands impressed her, small and rather delicate. Still, what could he possibly know about painting? Suppose he was without skill, and they were going to let him loose on their most treasured possession? She took him to the chapel and stood behind him, watching everything he did with apprehension.

'It's remarkable that the panel should have been so long in the chapel and never before treated. No one has been out to see it before have they?'

Cecile nodded. It was only within the last twenty-five years that the panel was thought to be something special, long-cherished by the order because it had come with the original deeds to the founding abbey in Saumur, no one thought until this century that it might be of any worth.

In the chapel some early girls were making prayers for intentions before beginning the school day. Cecile noticed how the bowed heads lifted as the man walked past. And he was not like Sister Joseph's film star, in fact, a man could not have been further from the ideal. He was at least two inches shorter than her.

She watched as he spread out his suitcase on one of the chapel benches, he looked like a tramp as he started to pull brushes, rags and packages out. He took a small brass holder with several eyeglasses and a small battery powered torch from his jacket pocket. He seemed to have forgotten her presence. She sat on a bench from which she could see Saint Polycarp pointing to his chest. The frame was magnificent, a heavy carved piece of solid wood that had required batons and supports to fix it into place over their small altar. The frame threatened to overshadow the painting it surrounded, and the image itself was dark with age. The solitary saint stared out. His pale torso gleamed in stark contrast to the brown background. Flames rested at his feet in a static, spiked pattern and high overhead flew a pale and ghostly dove. Some vague background buildings made up the rest of the composition.

It was the saint's face which always intrigued her. After

a long life he must have been relieved to show where the fatal spear would go. At his feet, undamaged by the fire, lay a mitre and crozier.

The restorer walked right up on to the altar. She stopped herself from saying something. After all he had to get close to the panel. She should have thought of that. The red lamp denoting God's presence was lit. To him it was just a light, an ornament no doubt. It was not that he was being disrespectful, he simply did not know. But then a change seemed to come over him. He moved quickly, hardly spoke except to ask for things, not impolitely but with the air of someone who expects efficiency. Without a glance backward he asked if it was possible to get some tepid water. And she rushed to fetch it, caught up in his urgency. He worked without stopping. She brought him a stool so that he could get closer to the top edges. She handed it to him, going right up on to the altar herself, and her hands were full so she could not bless herself for the transgression. She watched his back and admired his concentration. Now that was something like it. When he turned around his face was flushed with pleasure and she felt uncomfortable because she was staring.

'It's wonderful,' he said. 'I'm really fortunate, and honoured to be able to work on it. It's remarkably early you know, I think it might be fourteenth-century.'

What made him think that? She had suspected that it was a copy of an early style.

'It's been heavily restored. Perhaps around the turn of the century. That's when the worst damage would have been done.'

'Damage?'

'Oh yes. Pigments not made stable, slapped across the surface, adhesives that turn to mould and take the image with it, corrosion set in by someone introducing the wrong materials at a later date. But I think that it is an original work, and somewhere under there, away from more recent hands, are the brush strokes of the first painter, the one who gave it life.'

A sharp bell sounded and he jumped.

'Whatever is that?'

The chapel emptied fast.

'First lesson,' she said, as the few girls scuttled out.

'That's a terrible noise,' he said, and turned such a smile with his teeth in all directions that she decided there was no harm in him, and probably a lot of good. It was his enthusiasm which impressed her. And not everyone could be Catholic.

After that, she saw him daily, walking along the corridor to and from the chapel. He brought a colleague with him. A big, lumbering fellow. She kept out of their way as well as she could. It was during one afternoon when she was teaching her sixth-form that a girl was sent hurrying to her, one of the second years who ought to have been at games but had elected to 'help out', the euphemism for those who loathed sports.

'Sister Cecile, Sister Cecile, Reverend Mother says that you are wanted in the chapel, straight away.'

She felt ill. Her first instincts had been correct, the restorer did not know what he was doing, the panel was destroyed . . . a foot had gone through the surface, that great heavy colleague had sat on it . . .

'Did Reverend Mother say what it was about?' She pretended not to be agitated, looking over her shoulder at the girl while continuing to write on the board.

'No, Sister. Only that you were to go immediately.'

'Very well. You may go.'

The girl sped out of the room.

'Please continue with the work set,' she told her class, yet outside she could not hurry. She knew something had gone wrong.

That was the week Alan Wainsworth was going to remove the central panel from the wooden door that held it into the altar. He needed to lay the painting flat. It was a job requiring much delicacy and lightness of touch. Although he had proved her assumptions wrong once before, she felt that, small wristed or not, a man could hardly have the correct feel for the task.

Her stomach was heavy as she reached the chapel. For some reason, several nuns had gathered already. Mr Wainsworth rushed up to her. It was that bad.

'Cecile,' he said forgetting her role and talking to her as he would to a colleague. He looked nervous, but not distressed. He was excited, he smiled. She did not speak but looked to where he pointed. There was no painting in splinters, no ruined surface, but instead a strange tubular carving that at first glance looked like a rolling-pin. Wooden, with some design on its surface.

'Pick it up,' he urged.

It was a carving of a tower, with turrets and windows cut into the surface in thin scratched lines. It showed no great workmanship.

'What is it, where did it come from?'

Reverend Mother stood with some other nuns.

'If it were to be authentic,' Sister Mary Magdalen said, waving her hands excitedly.

'Oh, yes . . . and because it's been in our possession for so long . . .' Sister Joseph added, 'it must belong rightfully to the order.'

Three or four lay sisters stood around nodding.

'Well, exactly,' another voice put in. 'Think of the money it might raise if auctioned.'

'Of course,' Mary Magdalen gushed, her arms like windmills. 'It could take care of all the restoration work, and more besides . . .'

Cecile felt her spirit sink. 'Forgive me Lord, for my despair,' she muttered quickly under her breath.

She heard the man talking to her.

'. . . down the pillar of the frame. When we removed the panel from the altar it felt unbalanced. One side kept tilting – just wasn't as heavy. Then, when we were removing the painting, I noticed that the underside of the frame was irregular. One of the side pillars turned out to be hollow. When the platform was removed I could see this strange object inside.

It must have been lodged there for safe-keeping. The frame wasn't made for this painting. I think it must have been put on later. If you look you'll see that some of it covered a large area of the picture that was clearly meant to be seen. It's an oddity, as if the frame became more important than the pictorial composition, so that its fine carving was allowed to obscure the painted image.'

Wainsworth glanced back to the painting which was lying flat on a table.

'The frame has caused those black marks, can you see? Where the pigment has discoloured. I'm afraid that there are details we just can't read anymore.'

Cecile stared. She did not speak.

'Isn't it wonderful Sister Cecile,' Reverend Mother said, with a smile of genuine delight. Cecile nodded.

'I thought Sister, that as you have the keys to the library cases, we might keep the find there, and bring it to the attention of the governors during the week of the anniversary, by when you might have been able to discover a little more about it.'

Reverend Mother was offering her time to delve, and she had a case study. Was it authentic? If it was, and had been hidden so long – how many historians could ask for that?

'I have arranged for another member of staff to drill the girls for the pageant,' Reverend Mother said. It was something which Cecile would never have requested herself. She could not believe her luck. She prayed with gratitude that evening.

Later that same night Cecile took the strange item back with her to her stock-room. She shook it stupidly like a money box. She hardly understood what she was doing. She put it down upon her desk. It should be under lock and key. She knew she had no right to treat it so.

The carvings were crude. This was no great once-gilded reliquary, but possibly a mould for a metal outer casing. That was all. Then why go to such great lengths to hide it, the cheap, wooden centre of the valuable outer skin? The precious work long lost or looted in raids by the godless. Golden infidels who hunted bright stones like magpies, smashing and crushing to add a few pieces to their hoard.

Cecile stood up, holding her bunch of keys. Then a terrible thing happened. The hem of her sleeve swept the top of the wood as she moved and it rolled off the table before she could catch it. She heard a crack. The reliquary lay on the floor.

The top was split, a circular hoop had come away as a lid might. Cecile felt ill and wretched. These things ought to be in the possession of the government, not kept by irresponsible individuals. Yet here she was, the selfish owner of a piece of the past. She knew that she was old, she was clumsy, a liability with a frail body. Who knew the state of her mind? Was it equally weak? She did not know. She forgot things and grew tired. Only yesterday she told Sister Joseph about the choir practice and the nun had looked at her and remarked that she was becoming too efficient.

'You sent me a note on Monday.'

Cecile said nothing because she could not remember.

She stooped now to lift the fractured wooden tube and, as she did, noticed something. It was hollow. It had been light enough, and she had not imagined it to be solid, but she had not expected it to contain anything. Inside she could see something. A tightly scrolled piece of parchment. She eased it out gently and saw that packed under this was a stone, and a piece of lead, which rolled out onto her desk. A pilgrim's badge, the saint so worn that it had been rubbed away, but a human shape and behind it a wall.

A smile spread over her face. The delight of a child discovering another sweet in the empty bag. Here was a cache of simple things, a tight bundle of parchment to pack down a stone, and a badge. There was nothing marvellous about any of these things, she knew that pilgrim badges were common enough not to raise any financial hopes for Reverend Mother. No, it was the joy of discovery and the mystery of it all. She could slide the top back into place; the wood was not damaged. The object looked exactly the same. She put the stone, badge and parchment into her desk drawer, praying that she did no wrong by keeping silent, because she knew that she must have them just a while longer. Later that evening she locked the empty wooden roll back inside the library case.

That term her teaching was inspired. She revelled in the dissemination of knowledge. But alone at night she would take out the strange things and look at them, knowing she could not say anything about their discovery yet. She knew that she was practising deceit, but she did not want to announce them until she had spent time in contemplation. She would sit touching them, feeling them almost burn her hands. They were the living examples of history, ordinary, commonplace and puzzling. She would hold the plain lead badge in her palm until it felt heavy and she grew as weary as the pilgrim who journeyed for weeks in appalling conditions. She felt the touch of centuries, and the stone seemed to shimmer. At first she thought it no more than a pebble, a piece of rock, picked up long ago and placed inside this wood. It was smooth, polished. A black stone. She had seen nothing like it before. She felt it with nervous fingers. One side was flat with scratches. It was worn away, but she began to think that there might have been carving. Some type of amulet possibly. A magic stone used by necromancers to ward off evil and ill-health like a prescription.

She held it and it seemed to glow when warmed by her body heat. At first she thought it only black but the more she studied it the more she could see; blue lights, pale purple reflecting the inside of a pearly shell, iridescent and lovely. Where could this have come from? She wondered if its purpose had been practical or decorative. It was a good solid weight, satisfying as it lay in the palm of her hand like a veined worry-egg. Somewhere it picked out light and sent it back. Now it seemed a riot of colour. She wondered how she had not seen this at once, or could ever have thought it black. She turned it this way and that. And it caught her eye, reflected it, and seemed to look back at her. A hard stone stare which she had disturbed from sleep. From its surface that eye watched its surroundings.

Those scratches on the back did not feel haphazard. Two straight lines, erect as walls. Always there. She turned it over and looked intently. Was it a crude design? A house, a building of sorts? This must have been an amulet, to keep the bearer safe. Cecile's fingers closed around it and she did not want to put it down but rested like that without moving. She closed her eyes. Her breathing was shallow. Anyone coming upon her might think she was asleep or in a trance. It was as if another hand held the stone and brought it out of darkness. Then she was peaceful.

Throughout that term Reverend Mother stuck to her position. Cecile must still spend time in common, reduced to forty-five minutes, but time nonetheless to hear the voices of her sisters; to be among them not only at meals and common prayer.

Yet as she sat embroidering poppies in recreation her eyes glowed with pleasure. She began to enjoy the stitching as the border spread out in front of her, for while her hands were occupied her mind was free. Often while engaged in the task of needlework difficulties that she encountered would play over in her head, and many times a surprising new solution would force its way through.

Reverend Mother took the discovery of the wooden container as a sign that God wanted Cecile to work on her own special talent after a lifetime of humility. And Cecile was quick to grasp this. But Reverend Mother was anxious. Often a shadow would cross her face as Cecile appeared, Cecile always rushing to return to her cubby hole in a way that she did not rush to prayer.

All the while the restorers worked steadily, stripping layers of grime, centuries of grease and foul breath. Wainsworth gently prised off the aches of generations which encrusted the image of the early martyr.

'Would you mind talking to the girls about the work? I'm sure it's fascinating,' that was how Miss Barlock the art teacher had approached him. 'I've got a very good lower-sixth group. It would be so good as part of their art history session. Would you? If you have some free time?' She laughed nervously and put her hand to her mouth. 'Whoops, silly me! Asking if you're . . . well, you know . . .'

'Free?' he said.

'Oh, well you know what I mean. Bit rude of me, dearie me . . .' She flapped her hands.

He felt so awkward that he agreed on the spot. A week later the group faced him in the chapel.

'The wooden panels were ground and covered with layers of size, a type of glue. Each layer left to dry before the next was applied. This made the wood less porous, gave the panel a watertight coating. They used to use anything up to seventeen layers, just imagine that,' he said.

'Size was made from animal bones, sheep or goats.'

There was tittering. He glanced round. 'What do you think glue is made from today?' he looked surprised. 'Have you never heard the expression, "the horse ended up in the glue factory"?'

There was silence. Siobhan listened. She always thought it was something to do with chemicals, rubber or plants.

'There are different types of adhesives, but one of the ingredients still used in many is animal bone.'

Wainsworth looked around at the group of sixth-formers. His talk was not going well. Most of them looked bored and he had only started. How would he keep them interested for half an hour? He wished he had not agreed to talk to them, but their teacher had been turning up in the corridor for days before she had asked him. At the end of school she would be waiting in the staff room with questions, asking for information about one type of painting or another. He told her that he was a restorer, not a historian, although that was a lie. But this is where his lie had got him. He continued.

'After all this preparation, even then, the board was not ready to be painted. Nails were driven in to all the joins, cross-pieces of wood joined on to the back for strength, sometimes strips of metal. If a nail head protruded it would be coated in tin, so that it might not rust and show through. Everything was hammered flat, then ground again, and re-sanded until the surface was smooth.'

'And then the artist could begin?' a girl asked.

'Indeed not. Strips of cloth were then placed on top of the wood, like a sort of undergarment, and varnished or glued to the surface. Bandages, old table cloths, shirts, anything that could be torn up into strips was used. It was a coating of rags.

'On top of this was applied a layer of fine, white gesso. That is like a thin type of plaster. This would be allowed to dry thoroughly then another layer would be applied. Again the procedure would be repeated until four or five coatings of gesso had dried, one on top of the other. This final layer would be left to dry, usually out of doors in the sun, and the surface would be sanded down once more until a perfectly white, almost papery surface was the result. Only after this could the artist begin.'

That should make them think. If they couldn't just go and get something to work on, if they had to prepare a canvas first, let them think on that, how much a craft it was, how it was taught as part of a guild system. Let them see the labour involved in producing anything. Some things are still with us today because it was usual to prepare materials methodically. He did not like modern art, or artists. Individualists most of them. Raving about their personal angst. What about a bigger, collective concern? What about having some respect for the past, at least understanding what had passed before? He glared at his audience. He was sure some had fallen asleep.

'In many cases, where the panels have survived without an image, we can learn almost as much about the artist's studio from the preparations as we can from a surviving painting. For example, different types of glues were used in different regions, so it is often possible to locate a work through the foundations.

Then there's the strips of cloth themselves. Often tablecloths of extraordinary beauty have survived, in fragments. Sometimes we find finely embroidered sections of clothing, and so forth, helping us to gather a picture of the times.'

He looked around.

'Any questions?'

There was silence. Miss Barlock shuffled over to thank him for an interesting talk. And a hand went up, belatedly, with that wonderful thing: a question. A dark girl, who apologised before she spoke and hoped that he did not mind her asking, but what made him want to become a restorer? So he briefly talked about qualifications. No one was interested in the substance of his talk.

At recreation Cecile sat embroidering the poppies along the border of the cloth. Poppies made you drowsy, poppies were narcotic – they inched along the border. The more she worked the heavier their scent became, pulling her down into sleepy forgetfulness, round and round the scalloped edge. Lulling her and letting her mind dream. Strange feeling of being cold somewhere and working with a needle and the prick of bright blood on her fingers, the cloth held away from her so the stain would not mark the pattern. Salt into the callouses of her hands, old and worn. Stitched for a wealthy patron as a debt of honour, the cloth was her duty and her training piece. In Belgium the nuns made fine lace sailor-collars for the orphans. The pride of Bruges was the nuns' handiwork. The old altar robes, and the serving cloths embroidered and couched by so many sisters, painfully, in cold corridors, for the greater adornment of God, for the priest's back. And suddenly she felt angry, felt the sharp pin-prick as the needle punctured her finger and she saw the faint trickle of blood.

'You should always use a thimble,' her governess had said when as a small girl she was instructed in arts appropriate for her sex. She was educated at home along with her sisters. Times change. She could play the piano and draw passably well by the age of fourteen. But she wanted to be a historian, she knew even then. She turned her back on her real calling, imagining the flight into ecstasy her love of God would provide. And now it was too late to change direction. She sucked her finger in silence.

Wainsworth hated giving talks, he was better at his silent work. He had an instinctive feel for it. He recognised brushstrokes, different grains, later work by someone left handed, devil's branch. He laughed at the superstitions of ages.

He and his colleague moved the painting into the sacristy. Arturo Belli could not relax when on an altar. Wainsworth laughed, but felt relieved to be away from the exposed stage, where he had recently become aware that the lowered eyes of those praying occasionally rose to watch him.

In the last few weeks since Arturo joined him he had felt as if he had another male ally.

'Put it down to my Catholic background,' the Italian joked, 'but for God's sake let's get off this. I feel I ought to go round with communion.'

They talked more in those few weeks than they had before, as if the painting was exerting an influence on them. Arturo had teenage daughters himself, he was too old for any of the girls to watch him the way they did Wainsworth.

'I would never send my own to convent school I tell you,' he remarked one day, safe in the sacristy.

'My father had a boyhood of segregation in Italy ... I suppose Catholicism is the same the world over. When I was small we would travel to stay with my grandparents in Apulia; I never felt their home was different to ours in England, the same deep-felt beliefs.'

The smaller man had never thought of religion before, nor even of Arturo as a Catholic.

'Do you still practise?' he asked wondering why religion had become a topic now after months of working in the same department and never thinking about it.

He liked to think that he was without religion, free of its constraints and intellectual traps. Today he felt strangely rootless. Religion was nothing but history, the vast spread of humanity that revealed itself in the careful peeling back of centuries when he worked. But with faith, a work had greater significance.

'I don't bother,' the big man said. 'My wife is a church-goer, but I'm neither a disbeliever nor a believer, I'm caught somewhere in the middle.'

'But you must feel the significance of symbols in painting?' he said.

'Not really, no more than you do with an art historian's training. That's what I am primarily.'

'Does it mean much to you, this example of martyrdom?'

'That I couldn't say. It makes me angry, at the loss of life, and its veneration in death, when sometimes it might not be worth living. I went to the male equivalent of this place when I was at school, that's why I'd never inflict these places on my children. You've seen the way the girls look at you. Not me. I'm too old, too like their fathers, but you . . .' He thought for a while. 'These places are unhealthy, take my word for it . . .' he said and bent over the panel to reapply solution on cotton wool at the far corner.

Round and round in gentle, caressing circles his enormous hands worked to reveal another layer. Wainsworth watched, thinking that he worked in a manner which was almost reli-gious; that was the only word he could think of to describe it.

7

UNSETTLING

WAINSWORTH WOULD WATCH THE big man sometimes and wonder at his gentleness. When he was bent over the frame his wrists moved in the kindest of circles. His touch was constant, like a caress, and his eyes seldom moved from the image. He was like one hypnotised.

It struck Wainsworth that he dwelt on every detail like a lover. The sole entity in the world beyond himself. A moment of passion when outside all reality dissolves, nothing matters.

He was like those painted saints transfixed by the vision of God, like the disciples on the mount who saw Christ in glory and were altered beyond knowing.

He was a heavy man and the day, while not warm, had a closeness about it which made him slow. The radiators, old Victorian heating systems painted dullest brown, had only recently been opened. They smelt like bad drains and seemed to burn the dust which lay on them. They stood at odd places about the building, crude and ugly against the walls of the corridors and awkward in the wooden panelled study or heavy against the wainscoted walls of the main school. Here they were painted to match the wainscoting and like it were greasy with the smell of linseed. Wainsworth was sure that was the smell and he should know linseed from grape-nut or fish oil. The corridors reeked of it.

There were no windows that could be opened. In the sacristy

they were nailed down and the closest ones in the corridor had broken sash-cords.

The big man straightened up. He groaned and rolled his shirt sleeves to his elbows. He did not notice his colleague who watched as he wiped his hands on a greying towel.

'Everything feels so dusty this morning,' he announced suddenly. 'I can't get enough air.'

He threw his arms wide and breathed deeply. Arms which were dark haired like a monkey's moved in and out, keeping pace with his breathing and he turned his white hairless palms upwards. He was fat and ungainly with too much of the corporeal about him, his soft paunch deadened with wine.

Wainsworth felt the wizened white figure of Saint Polycarp watch them from the panel, the ribs painted in Byzantine rows like the pleats of the coy garment which concealed his nudity, the taut legs showing beneath. One finger pointed languidly to his chest. In the background, a dim row of shadowy buildings. A white dove flew upwards. A bishop's mitre lay discarded. Arturo's belly moved from side to side as he walked over to the window.

The younger man wondered what the big fellow would have been like twenty years earlier, before he knew him. He was probably never thin. No, not like he was, or like the saint whose belly was concave, a dark ridge of shadow along the hollow where his disciplined guts were. He watched as Arturo loosened his tie then took it off altogether to open his shirt to his waist. His chest, like his arms, was afforested with thick, dark hair. The younger man felt the irony of such a luxury of growth there while the head was bald. Age mocked everyone.

'It's all right for you,' the big man said. 'When you bend over the work you don't get this in the way.' He prodded his stomach.

'You can work more comfortably than me at this stage. You're all bones. That's England for you. You don't eat, you English. Miserable so and so's,' and he started to laugh.

The small man's concentration was broken, but so was his colleague's.

'Arturo, you were dreaming,' he warned him.

'What if I was?' the big man shrugged. 'My father always said that. Said I'd get nowhere.'

He seemed to be deep in thought. There was a short silence, then he spoke again.

'But there are ways of dreaming, you know, ways of dreaming . . .'

'What do you mean?'

'Eh? Oh, like when something stops you for the first time, you know pulls you up sharply and makes you pay it attention, then you walk about in a daze after, fixated. You're hardly dreaming. More awake I'd say.'

He wiped his brow. Perspiration glistened.

'I can remember seeing my first real painting – you know the way you study things from books and suddenly, the real thing is there in front of you. I was a student. I was in Italy between the wars, staying with my father's family for the summer. God, I feel old,' and he laughed again.

'What was it then, your first painting?'

The big man looked past Wainsworth, as if he saw the image again.

'It was a Simone Martini. A beautiful, beautiful thing. "The Annunciation". A medieval work of the Trecento. It hangs in the Uffizzi. Have you seen it?'

'I don't recall it, I know some of his work is in Sienna.'

'Yes, in the Palazzo Pubblico. But you would know it if I had a book to show you. It dazzled, sort of shone. Can you imagine that?

'I travelled up to Florence to stay there for a week. Give my aunt a break as much as anything, she was worn out with me, their peculiar English nephew. I kept going back to the gallery. I remember standing, just standing . . . I was awestruck. And each day there was something else that captivated me.' He shot Wainsworth a glance, as if he had been discovered doing something he would prefer to keep private. 'Oh well, we never recapture that first enthusiasm.'

'Describe it, will you? The painting. It's going to drive me mad until I can recall which one you mean.'

But Arturo said that it was an annunciation in gold, with words standing out in relief, and there were many works of that nature.

'I could have put my hand out and touched it, my fingers could have traced those words, it was so solid, and so real. And when I walked to the hotel I swear I don't remember getting there. I heard no traffic, no clatter of wheels on the cobbled road. I thought about the donor. I imagined him opening his purse, the chink of coin as he paid to be immortal.'

'Who was the donor?'

'Eh? God knows.'

Wainsworth started to laugh.

'That's Italy for you.' Arturo grinned.

'My father became a religious fanatic as he grew older. He ran a pastry shop in Kendall. My mother's from there. He used to make these great cakes for baptisms. Italians love their bellies. I always thought the Duomo looked more like a giant meringue with those great stripes of green and pink, like sugared icing. We make frosted basilicas like gingerbread houses. That's not architecture, it's domestic science.'

Wainsworth laughed.

'But my father was an artist. You should have seen some of the things he made; birds, flowers – all colours – out of spun sugar. He was good, I'll give him that, and a business-man. When the local convent was running down he got round there and bought up the press for the communion wafers and supplied all the Catholic churches. And he wasn't a bigot, he did the big plaited loaves for harvest festival at chapel. He'd do barmitzvahs, anything.' He scratched his face and grinned, remembering.

'He was a terrible smoker with a yellow finger. I thought it was hereditary when I was a lad, this stain like a birthmark. I thought I'd get one when I came to manhood.'

'He never smoked in the shop. He used to nip out for a quick one. He'd be standing in the street leaning on the window, ended up having to shout orders into the kitchen. Mother wouldn't let him in. All our ceilings downstairs were ruined with nicotine. Then one day after it had rained for nearly a week and he was wet through standing outside, he went to the priest who offered to pray for him.'

'What happened?' Wainsworth leaned against the wall.

'Oh, he tried to stop smoking before and never managed. So the parish priest had masses said, and we were all embarrassed every Sunday hearing his name read out at mass for special intentions, and all the neighbours watching him wondering what they were. And the old man gave up. He never let another cigarette pass his lips. Of course, he said it was a miracle.'

'I suppose people develop their religious convictions through all sorts of emotional shock,' Wainsworth ventured.

'Emotional shock? He nearly gave my mother one. He was up at five every day as it was for the gas ovens to be warmed – now he's off to first mass every day and the fires not lit. Still, it got him the order for the communion wafers.' Arturo flexed his arms. 'I'd reckon we've more strange sad men in our clergy than in any other faith.'

'Why do you feel that?'

The big man shrugged.

'It's like smoking, religion plays havoc with your health. My dad just wasn't the same man after . . .' he did not finish and shook his head. 'Pass me that brush will you?' he said looking down. 'Anyhow, you live the life of a monk. You'd make a right grand martyr,' he suddenly joked. 'You remind me of this soft bugger,' and he pointed disrespectfully at the panelled saint.

'We love martyrs, us Catholics, because they've risen above their bodies. Left all that behind. You want to get out, go dancing, anything,' and he winked. Wainsworth felt uncomfortable and made no reply.

When he got home that evening he pulled books down

until he found a small reproduction of the Martini painting Arturo had spoken about.

He remembered it at once. The Virgin recoils from the angel's spoken words in horror. Her delicate white hand might try to push the message away, but there is no way to avoid her fate; she will accept.

'Behold the handmaid of the Lord,' but that will come later. It is not in this scene. Martini shows her fear. She loathes her fate even while she accepts it. She shrinks away from the unpleasant. The artist loves her humanity and rejoices in her revulsion.

What had Arturo called himself? Master Bun, the baker's son ... he said that even then he was turning to fat. But Wainsworth knew that in the rounded faces of angels Arturo must have seen the early respect for anyone well fed. A time when to have enough flesh was to have dignity. Well he too had a body as well as an intellect, or what the medieval world called a soul.

He put the book back carefully, then noticed a photograph album next to it. Idly he began turning pages. Photographs of people he had lost contact with after he moved to take up this job. Some faces he could not remember and had to read the dates on the back.

He was lanky when he was a student. Never good-looking, he had no doubts about that. But those dark glasses, how could he have worn them? Someone ought to have said something. He had no idea what had happened to any of those people he used to be with. It had never bothered him before.

Six years ago he had come to this provincial place. Most weekends he went on courses to do with work. He had not considered it before, but outside of his job he had nothing else. Even his closest friend he only saw occasionally whenever he returned to visit his parents in his home town. But up till now he used to believe he led a charmed life, able to do what he wanted, fortunate to work in an area that he loved.

He was free, independent. That was what he wanted. He

did not consider himself to be anti-social. He got along with people, but he had no close friend, no one he could talk to.

Everyone he knew seemed to be in the department. It was depressing that all he had in common with them was work.

He went into the bathroom and stared at himself in the shaving mirror.

'That beard is coming off.'

He walked into the bedroom and threw open the wardrobe.

'Look at them! I don't have to wear the same things day in day out.' He felt irritated. He bundled up a check jacket the colour of nothing and walked into the kitchen to put it in the bin. But he stopped. There are starving people in the world.

The jacket lay across the table. In the book-lined room that was a study and a lounge, and everything that he made it be out of necessity, he put plainsong on the record player. It always calmed him. Back in the kitchen he took a large bin-liner and threw the jacket into it.

'The charity shop then, first thing on Monday.'

With this intent he returned to his bedroom and emptied his wardrobe.

Next department party they have, I'm going to go, he told himself as he lay on the sofa, and what's more I'm going to dance at it, although I haven't for years.

Then he realised that he did not know how to. He laughed, it was time that he learned. He wanted to find that part of his youth which he had been terrified of participating in.

'You're a dark horse aren't you. I don't know what you get up to,' the big man said the following day.

'You've been smiling away to yourself all morning. Do you have a girlfriend? Are you courting or sommat?'

He did not blush this time, but grinned.

'No.'

'I don't believe you for a minute lad,' said the older fellow shaking his head.

'You ought to,' the smaller laughed good-naturedly and

thought how right Arturo had been when he told him that he imagined him sitting in night after night reading.

He did have a girlfriend when he was a student, when things like that were easier, but it had ended, simply enough. They had drifted apart, what with leaving college and going to work. He heard she went overseas. He laughed, but could not make the laugh work.

'Bloody Hell, I've seen that many of these young things looking after you. I know you think I'm kidding, and they're desperate here, so it's not much consolation, but if I was young again, without this,' he prodded his belly, 'I'd be out there every night of the week. I'd have them fighting over me.'

Both men laughed. The fat one rippled with the absurdity of it, his face became red and his eyes watered. Every time he stopped he would see the younger man grin and that would start him off again. Wainsworth put down his brush and wiped his eyes. Each time he looked at his colleague he imagined him surrounded by fighting women; warriors who could throw such a great bulk of manhood as easily as they liked, solid as sumo.

All afternoon he couldn't stop laughing. Between bouts he thought how some people had it worked out. To him, Arturo was happy. Nuns, too. They ignored the pleadings of the flesh until they no longer felt them.

For the first time in years he was tortured with some kind of physical ache, its root deep inside him. Even his dreams were unthinkable.

8

VOCATION

SIOBHAN UNPACKED HER SCHOOL bag carefully, making sure that she took out the books in the right order, the smallest first, the largest after so that the backs did not get caught together or crumpled as they were lifted out. She was careful in her work and, surprisingly, was neat in the care of her copy books, while the rest of her always gave the appearance of being hastily finished, out through the door at a run. She was always slightly late. It irked her.

Sister Cecile stressed the importance of punctuality, the value of five or ten minutes' extra work that could be squeezed into a day. She told the class that in the five minutes they waited for her to arrive they could have revised one of the mnemonics she gave out to help them recall dates, terms and events.

Siobhan loved the positive attitude Cecile had. One should always do everything fully. But sometimes that enthusiasm was hard to recapture. Away from school everything dwindled. Her spirits sank. There was no one she could talk to, no one she could trust enough to tell. In the telling it would sound worse, it would sound intentional when it was sudden, unpremeditated. She did not want other people's pity.

Her father never intended to hit her. It was not as if he doled out punishment which he considered her due. It was quick and desperate. She drove him to it. He had no choice.

Only last night her mother had screamed that it was all her fault as, clutching his heart, her father left the room.

Last night Siobhan stood up shakily from the floor where she tripped. He had hit her across the face and she slipped and went down. Her head throbbed, her vision was foggy and she overbalanced. She held on to the wall and willed the room to stop revolving. She heard her mother's shrill voice calling her, accusing her.

Upstairs she knew he would lie on the bed in the unlit room, groaning dramatically until his wife went to him. He had been warned about getting excited. She knew that one day as he argued with her he would probably die from the exertion, then her mother really would have an excuse to blame her.

The doctor had told her father to lose weight. That was a factor contributing to his heart condition.

'It's putting your heart under too much stress.'

' "So," says I to he, "Doctor Megaffy, isn't it children have our hearts broke? They're the cause of all our stress, without them we'd be healthy," and didn't the doctor look at me surprised? "Oh," says he, "I'd never have thought it for you Mr Doolin. Siobhan, now she's such a good girl." Says I, "Doctor you don't know the half of it ... she's a little ..." and didn't I just stop meself in time from saying something I'd only regret. "Doctor," says I, "she's that wild, I know what she is." '

Her mother turned to her with a smug look.

'There! Now even Doctor Megaffy knows the way you are. You can't hide. I'll let everyone know the carry on we have here with you, Miss Knowall.'

'Ah, she's that bloody sullen,' her father agreed.

That was how the row began. She said nothing. Her mother and father sat facing the television. They tutted and frowned as they watched her out of the corner of their eyes. They were drinking tea. They crashed their cups down on to saucers, swearing every time they saw her. She sat cold as a statue. She had no right to be there. She had homework to do, so she left the room silently. And that was just the start of it.

She was half-way up the stairs when the door was flung open behind her.

'Come down here this minute! You stuck up little bitch! Get down here, I'll give you permission to leave the room!'

There was no point in arguing so she came down slowly.

'I'll teach you to leave the room without permission.' Her mother's eyes glowed.

'I've never heard you ask to leave the room,' Siobhan said coolly and knew that had done it.

There was the sound of an explosion from the sofa as he leapt to his feet.

'Don't you talk back to your mother, you little bitch. From now on you will ask me every time you want in a room, and every time you want out, understand?'

His face was red, his chest heaved. He was an enormous man, towering over her mother who stood at four foot ten. He cast a squat shadow over Siobhan, suffocating her. She retched.

'Understand?' he boomed.

'What?' she asked and feigned boredom.

The rumbling of his system grew louder as he approached white heat. Quivering, she stood her ground. She pretended not to have noticed anything.

'You little snob!'

The hand came down across the side of her face. An enormous hand. Her cheek burned.

'Understand?' The question was screamed on the outrush of breath.

'What?' she was blinking, her voice hard edged. 'What?'

Her father was a steam driven machine. The next inhalation moved the hand up, it swung over his shoulder for leverage and on the exhaled breath came down full force on the opposite side of her face.

Siobhan's left foot slipped, she balanced but the hand hit again from left to right. She felt herself fall. Her ears rang now as air was slapped into them. She closed her eyes so that she would not see him. He stooped over and continued to strike, then, because his heart was bad and he was unfit, the bending being too hard for him, he stopped.

A voice that was not human screamed, 'Understand?' prolonged and grotesque. A question she would never answer. It screamed wanting power. She bit her lip . . . never.

She lay rigidly. There was a stillness as there always was at the end. He had exhausted himself. Moaning with fatigue, for it was the only exercise he took, he ran his hands through his hair and left the room, clutching his heart as he passed his wife.

Her ears sent buzzing noises deep inside her head. Sometimes it lasted for hours, then she would become frightened that the sounds might never stop and she would be left for ever listening to interference while everyone around her would have to speak up.

'Now look what you've done. You've made your father ill!' Her mother's voice was far off. Siobhan got to her feet. She held on to the wall. Everything span.

The only thought in her mind was that she would have to do her homework or she would get into trouble at school.

Later, in her room she timed herself by the alarm clock. Half an hour and her ears still hummed. They ran with wax. It was almost an hour before they stopped this time. One day, that man would make her deaf. Only one more year she thought and they would have no rights over her. She would escape on her eighteenth birthday, just disappear. That was the dream which sustained her.

School at least helped. She left early most days and did not return until she had to. She spent as little time at home as she could. If she sat quietly downstairs her mother would come into the room, glare at her and tell her that she made her sick, sitting there like Lady Muck. The day before when she went into the kitchen to get her food, her mother asked her did she think they ran a hotel?

Her mother had not cooked her a meal since her fifteenth

birthday. That was a celebration not to be forgotten.

'You're too old to be waited on like royalty.'

She wanted to get far away, go to another place where no one knew her. Where her parents could not find her. Maybe she was unnatural, because she could not love either. But then the idea of love was unreal. It was for greater things, not for people. It was for God and for ideals, for something bigger.

She must have loved them when she was little, surely. All children love their parents. But she could not remember. It seemed as if the only emotion allowed was anger. Her father's anger was a crazed animal that he could not control. Once he told her that he always asked God to forgive him, that he always had to say a little prayer after he hit her. It didn't help. And her mother was angry with her for not being the son she wanted and for still being at school.

'You're stuck up since you've been at that place,' she would hiss.

Siobhan said nothing. To venture opinions was madness. Like the time she dared to suggest that the pope was not always right, that he was human and must make mistakes occasionally, and her father clouted her swearing that the pope was infallible.

'We'll have no more of that bloody communist talk in this house. This is a Catholic household and you'll abide by its rules.'

The first rule was silence. She sat in corners listening to them talk. Maybe her mother was right when she called her stuck up. They were boring. She listened to them and it seemed that they never had anything interesting to say to each other. She'd rather be a snob than a bore.

She crept around rooms so that they might not hear her, she kept out of their way, but still she could not manage every day to avoid a confrontation. It was the only time her father spoke to her, it was the only time she was touched. A ritual as insistent as mass. She wondered why she did not become hardened, but she hated the rows with a new and shocking freshness each time. She would have given anything to become cold. Instead she was horrified by the severity of her feelings. Her mother was right in many ways, one day she might indeed murder her father.

'You're killing your father!' That was what she had screamed at her as she hung on to the wall, scared to move.

'One of these days he's not going to recover. I'll have you taken out of that bloody school and you can clear out of this house and get yourself a job, bloody well learn to look after yourself, learn some housewifery, that's what you should be doing instead of prancing around with those spoilt girls at that place. When I was your age I'd been working for three years. I was earning my keep, like you should be. Start bringing home the money, then you can have a say!'

Her mother had looked like an athlete psyching up before a race.

'I'm going to write to the headmistress. It's unhealthy all those women together, they're peculiar. I'll say I'm bringing you out of that school. Get out! Get out of my sight! You make me sick! You make me . . .' but the last word had been inaudible.

At the end of the school day, Siobhan developed the habit of going to the junior common room where, from the window, she would watch the others racing out as the bell sounded. When it was quiet she would go to the library to get through some of her homework. At least she could manage half of it before going home, get it out of the way before the rows started. Sometimes whole evenings were lost to her, even when the row ended, when her father went quiet or stalked out of the room leaving her alone, she could not settle. She would feel like a shaking wreck, unable to concentrate. She loathed her father for that. That was when he had won no matter how calm she looked, no matter that she did not cry, shout back and lose her precious glassy front.

She visualised herself like the iceberg that sunk the *Titanic* on its maiden crossing, solid and unconquerable, but she felt the fissures widen with successive washings of salt. They carved paths inside, cut her harder and more viciously than any blow.

She understood that to escape she must work, work and make something of herself. She did not know what, only that she must do it at all costs.

She dreaded weekends. Early on she joined the netball team so that she could get away to matches on Saturdays. Then, when she was fifteen and three months, just the age to get her yellow national insurance cards, she found herself a Saturday job. That was even better because with the money she could go to a film after work. She didn't care what she saw. She would sit through it twice, killing time before going home. She lived on sandwiches at the weekend. On Sunday her mother occupied the kitchen, steaming with irritation. Siobhan did whatever was quickest just to get out of her way but still her mother would remark that she was eating them out of house and home.

She remained in her room all day on Sundays. After the tortuous ritual of mass together she would walk home quickly. She lived a half existence at home. It was like a game, but it had been taken too far and none of them knew how to stop. It was as if she was no longer there, she was a shadow that did not show up in family photographs. She congratulated herself on her unobtrusiveness.

She was proud, she would not ask them for anything. Her mother told her on her fifteenth birthday that she would have to begin paying for her food, but her father put his foot down at that, and said did she want the girl to be starved or what, so the kitchen was not put out of bounds. But her mother let her know that she resented every mouthful of food she ate.

She trudged home leadenly.

'I don't know what you get up to at that sodding school. What keeps you there till almost six o'clock? I see other kids coming home at half past four?' Her mother was irritated.

'I've been helping Sister Cecile with the stock. There's always something that needs doing.'

Siobhan visualized the shelves of books that still had to be gone through, boxes to be opened, rubbish to be moved.

'Siobhan, would you help me with some labelling after school, if you're not in a hurry?' Cecile had asked her one day, after noticing her in the library on a few occasions. For Siobhan it was perfect, another excuse to stay away from home.

Much of the history stock was being transferred downstairs, to be stored in a huge free-standing cupboard that had been donated to the convent. Now that her teacher was busy working on private research many of the practical tasks were delegated. Siobhan would volunteer, but was sensible enough not to want to make a spectacle of herself. She would catch up with Sister Cecile out of class and tell her that she did not mind staying behind.

'Don't your parents worry about you coming home a bit late? Won't your tea be spoiled?' she asked, and the girl had started to say something but changed half way.

'We eat late,' was what she finally said.

'When do you do your homework?'

'I try to do some of it here, the rest I do later in the night after . . .'

'After you've eaten,' Cecile had finished the sentence off.

'Yes, after eating,' she said and thought the nun looked at her too closely.

'You think more of that school and toffee-nosed teachers than you do of your own parents,' her mother said the night before.

'We're not good enough for you any more.'

Her mother blamed the school for everything. 'Ever since you went to that school,' became a stock phrase. Siobhan affected indifference. Her mother would get wilder and wilder and make outlandish threats which both knew she would never carry out.

'I'll have you taken away from that bloody school, it's

that place has got you high and mighty. I'll go round there tomorrow and tell them that you're leaving to get a job instead of wasting any more time.'

She had to get through school, it was the first step. Her mother baited her with her one real fear. She hated how that threat was wielded. And yet she knew that her father wanted her to do well academically. Like all people who have never done well at the business of education, he had an inflated sense of what it meant. He wanted the prestige of having his child at university.

Siobhan was tired of her mother's threat. That evening she turned her head and looked at her. She agreed. It was a good idea.

'I think you're right,' she said, controlling her voice. 'Why should I stay at school when I could be out earning money? I could be going out every evening enjoying myself, I could buy decent clothes and make-up and go to the hairdresser. I've seen a coat I'd really like, I would be able to afford it if I wasn't at school. I hate having no money, no good things. I could ask if the shop will take me on full time. I'll ask the manager when I go in on Saturday. OK?'

Her mother looked stunned, but nodded her head.

As her father came into the room Siobhan smiled at him.

'Dad you'll have to write to Reverend Mother.'

He looked puzzled.

'About me leaving school halfway through the term.'

'What?' he exploded.

Siobhan smiled.

'It's OK. Mum and me have been working it out. She reckons I'd be better off leaving school and working. She thinks it's all a waste of time this education lark, don't you Mum?'

Over by the sink her mother grew smaller, and Siobhan regretted what she had started, but it was too late to change her line now.

'How can you be so stupid!' he shouted. 'I thought you had more sense,' he said, turning to Siobhan.

'I thought at least you had more sense than your mother.'

He slammed his hand down on the draining board.

'Is that what you want for her? Because you went straight into the factory, does that mean we can't have something better for her? You're a stupid woman.' He turned his back on his wife. When he looked at Siobhan his eyes pleaded.

'At least you try and get the education I never had.'

Siobhan for the first time that she could remember wanted to hug him.

'Are you going mad putting ideas like that into her head or what? Do you want her to grow up as ignorant as you!'

The woman swung around, and struck wildly at him.

'I don't want her to be stuck up, that's what!'

'Grow up for Jesus' sake woman,' he spat, and she shrieked hard and loud as if she had been struck.

'Get out! Get out! Don't you tell me to grow up, I can't stand the pair of you.'

Siobhan felt sick. More than anything, she hated when they argued with each other. Then there were no winners in the end and she would be despised for witnessing them. She wished that she had not called her mother's bluff this time. She went to walk from the kitchen but the sound of plates smashing made her look around. A saucepan bounced off the sink and caught her full force on the forehead. She put her hands up. The kitchen was frighteningly silent.

'You fool! Look what you've done now! You could have blinded her.'

Siobhan felt the injustice of it. How dare he be angry at her mother just because for once he was not the cause of pain.

Her mother watched. When she spoke her voice was theatrical, callous among the pans and bottles.

'She's all right, she's just putting it on.'

But next morning her face was dark. Over her right eye was a small cut.

Her father had left for work when she came down and her mother tried not to look at her, pretending that she had forgotten about the previous night, but she poured Siobhan a cup of tea, the first time in two years. Siobhan looked at it, a silent peace offering. Slowly and deliberately she poured herself a glass of water and took two aspirin from the cabinet and swallowed them. In the bathroom she covered the mark with elastoplast, then without a word she left for school. The tea was untouched in the kitchen.

That morning the convent seemed like an oasis in her life. The nuns had a life of prayer and dignity, silence and respect that seemed to her the best way to be.

All the people she trusted, those who had made something of their lives, had dedicated themselves to an ideal, to something that held fast while everything else pulled and strained away. She thought her family were brutish, while others had dreams, ideals. She thought then that the ideas must be God. All was possible through his love. It gave expression to all the thoughts and ideas that had been building up. She was searching for some other meaning to life. God allowed her to ask her naïve questions without anger. How different this heavenly father was from her earthly.

She knew that she was doomed to an eternal round of violence and fighting, that was the reality of a godless world. That was the only life she had seen. There was no respect or privacy. She felt as if her parents would forever mock her, and their mocking made her mute. She thought how unfair it was that your silence was called your insolence. They would beat it out of you until you screamed as coarsely as they. Then they would have won as, shouting and swearing, you joined their spewing ranks, unable to feel, unable to think, unable to speak. Your voice yelled abuse, your fists battered. Your long insolent silence broken, you shrieked the battle cry of those cursed who speak in a wordless rush of noise, grunting and pointing without language and without reason.

'Dear God save me!' she prayed. The idea was crystallising. God was everything. A way out. A better existence.

'Dear God! Dear God!'

PART THREE

CUT IN STONE

9

THE DELEGATION FROM
THE CROWN OF THORNS

DESPITE HER HORROR OF the outside world, the abbess knew she would be expected to be one of the party to travel to the Sisters of Compassionate Darkness. As one of the youngest it would be unthinkable to send a less able-bodied sister in her place. And so, the night before she was to leave, she prayed in her cell. Dreading the journey in front of her, she asked for strength.

Ever since she had arrived at the Crown of Thorns she had had restless nights, haunted by dreams of noisy taverns and the strange houses she had seen. Her ears recalled shouts and weak screams from dark alleys when she had ridden through places which teemed with people as if every day was market day. She saw narrow habitations butted on top of each other, wallowing in vice and filth, belly to back like dogs. Places where there was no air to breathe, only the foul stink of decay and disease, the sour smell of sweat, of bodies in disgraceful proximity. And she had dreaded the men whose faces were loathsome and twisted as original sin.

It was decided that two abbesses plus herself, a scribe, a linguist and three lay sisters (including one good cook) from the Crown of Thorns would comprise the party.

It was the lay sisters who found them a guide. Without one they would never clear the mountain pass, nor the forest where a man might ride all day in a circle and never know it. Only local people, shepherds, could guide them through. But they could not trust anyone. They put it about the settlement that they wanted to engage an honest man without family because he would be away on a journey. But they saw only drunkards. There was no one devout enough for their purposes. Then a man approached them. His son, he told them, was as good as any, and might never speak of where he had been, or through easy talk let out that which they would not want known. Since birth he had not uttered one word.

'He's as silent as the ground,' the peasant said. 'A good strong lad of sixteen who as a babe made only mewling sounds like the weakest of cats. They thought to drown him, but the priest pronounced him healthy and baptised him. He's a Christian, without the devil in him,' the man said, 'and he'll be quiet on your account.' Then he laughed.

He presented his son later that same day at the convent porch. The young abbess remained behind a screen to scrutinise the pair. She was struck by the boy's appearance as he stood awkwardly behind his father. Although of average height he gave the impression of being smaller than he was, for he hunched his shoulders as if warding off a beating and stood guarded against blows.

His eyes were light, without any colour, his hair almost white, so fair a combination which caused people to remark that he was afflicted with moon-quiet.

While he had no learning, his father said he was not stupid. He could listen and understand well what was being asked of him. And if he overheard anything, what did it matter?

It was decided that the boy would wait outside the walls. Mother Superior gave a purse to one of the lay sisters, who counted out coins into the man's hand.

'Behave now, and do as you are told,' he said to the boy, and boxed his ears for good measure before walking away.

'It may be Hocktide before he returns to you. You shall receive money each Friday at this porch.'

'That suits fine, blessed sisters,' the man laughed, turning back to face them. 'You'll see he has his belly full?'

'All his needs shall be met. He shall be shod too.' The lay sisters stood back.

The man laughed again and looked at the three sisters, shaking his head from side to side at some joke.

'I'll be back each Friday then,' and he walked away without a backwards look, muttering and counting the coins in his palm, well pleased with the deal. 'Do as you like,' they heard him say. He guffawed and made to the side of the road leading to the tavern.

The boy was told to wait at a landmark, where later that evening a party would join him. They would tell him their destination and he would ride with them, and show them the terrain. He nodded and went away.

It had been decided that they ought to dress as men. They were to bare their heads and cut their hair short. In such garb it was hoped they might pass without molestation.

The night before departure, Aelreda removed her wimple and ran a hand through her prickly scalp where the last haircut bled her. It had been savage. She watched her shadow in the flat dish of the brass candle holder, but could not see herself. She smiled, imagining the others.

The next day they left when the sky was dark, waiting not even for matins. As the light eased they could each see their travelling companions, and they were a laughing group which rode through the outlying convent fields before any ploughman stirred. At the large rock on the hill they met their guide, handed over the extra mule and the boy looked surprised to see not sisters but a group of men.

Such a strange collection they made. They passed without words through towns looking so solemn that the townsfolk took them for bailiffs, or tax inspectors come to count windows, doors and drinking vessels. They prayed it would not be an increase in the tithe on horses. Behind the party rode an upright figure balancing a large, leather bound book in the saddle bag of the mount. That must be a ledger they told each other, the clerk is riding behind.

'It is a tax upon horses, if they can no longer afford to ride them,' they said, seeing that all the men rode mules.

And so the sisters passed without disturbance. All were glad when they did not dismount but continued through the habitation. They were hurried on their way to cries of, 'Godspeed you, sirs!'

Out on the mountain road the party was gay, the days cold but clear and the light, while it held, let them make good progress. But the nights were icy.

At first the abbess was shocked by the merriment of the party, who revelled in the open after years of enclosure. But among them her spirits were light. Life could be a source of delight not revulsion. God made life, and so it was sanctified. There was no sin in resting her eyes on the bare branches of trees against a white sky, or being shocked by the burst of colour from winter berries growing along the way. There was no shame in the bird-song which accompanied them as they journeyed, and the higher they went, the lighter she felt. Up above the world there was an extraordinary calm which lumbering night could not disturb.

This party was different; there was no rabble to deal with, no coarse speech, no need to distrust one's companions, no suggestive comments to make the blood boil in her face. Like a closely bonded family they travelled, wading icy streams their tunics rucked up; and the boy's shoulders would shake with silent laughter, until it was his turn and they teased him.

Each night they put up camp and slept through the dark. And their good, steady boy would question their strength to continue the next morning with a quizzical look, then kneel for a blessing before setting out, believing them gentle monks.

In the thin higher reaches, the sisters found breathing hard and used speech less and less, so that some days they were entirely silent. When they broke silence their voices were high and awkward.

They all suffered great dizziness at times, except the boy.

The abbess felt as if the world rushed past her. All the world seemed to move and the ground rumbled. Then she had to grip her mount to stay upright. Once he caught her just as she fell.

When her heart pounded in her chest during the hard stretches of the journey, she felt exhilarated. How different to those times in the convent when, with her back bent in dulling toil, she laboured. This work gave her spirit. This daily effort made her strong. Even when tired she felt at times that she could run and skip as any kid in a field, although she did neither after a lifetime of learning how to walk decorously for Christ.

The boy's colourless eyes watched her. She was haunted by his wordless stare. Speech simplified people. His muteness made him separate. She saw the world unfolding as he pointed. He did not delight in cruelty nor disturb creatures without purpose. On her earlier journey one fellow would entertain them by skinning live frogs, laughing as the creatures hissed in death. God's creatures.

She thought about her own convent. She knew that Scolastica was wrong; all life had to be respected. It was the methods, not the teaching, she could argue against. She was no match for the old nun, but the practice would be stopped when she returned.

She hoped that at the sight of the Virgin's girdle, some clear argument might come to her to sway Scolastica and let her understand.

Aelreda felt the strain of the journey. On the sixth night, after an endless stretch of uphill climbing, she felt worn and old. She discovered that she could endure until the daily movement became routine, until it felt as strange to her to be in the same place and recognise surroundings as once to be on the move had been disconcerting. She learned to identify distant shapes of hills which the boy pointed out. At first they seemed to shift, an interchangeable strip of something between earth and sky, but they became ridges, sharp outlines, familiar and comforting. They continued along their journey. The world was unknown land, pasture became wilderness, coarse grasses sprang up and the earth changed from green to brown. For an eternity this landscape continued, with sounds of life, the screech of the hawk, the whir of wings in an expansive sky. But without identity. This was the place where man was cast after the fall.

But it was not without beauty. She listened for the silence before dawn, for the deafening greeting from the sky at the first signs of the sun, and she welcomed it back, grateful that life would continue for a day. The sisters looked no further than to each night and prayed that day would follow.

Aelreda felt weak. She pushed her feet into each aching step. Why had it become so hard? She remembered the laughing parties of pilgrims, the fat merchants bloated on ale and gristle, pink as new hogs sucking at a teat. These were ready to seize what depravity they could; they hunted the gross, and their souls were doused in sin, as poor bread that wipes the inside of a bowl becomes sated with grease. They called that the beggar's share and sinful or not she would be grateful for a bite of that alone. She was no better than the lowest pilgrim, her mind did not dwell constantly on God, but on hunger and fatigue. There were times when she thought she could barter her soul for a long rest and something to eat.

Now a circle of pain swallowed her. It spread upwards into her back like the branches of a great tree, each new shoot agonising. This then was her purgatory. And she was terrified of Hell, for if it was worse than this, she knew she could not endure it.

They had ridden for barely two weeks when the weather broke. Thunderstorm followed thunderstorm. The stream overflowed, bursting out of its gully. The track turned into a river. Two of their mules fell and broke their ankles and were left drowning in green mud the colour of mould as the party continued on foot, the hems of their cloaks dragging, heavy with soil.

The boy was nimble footed but even he slipped occasionally and caught wildly at branches to keep upright. The ridge above the valley was particularly treacherous. To misplace a foot would mean instant descent. On the worst climbs the boy lashed them together with rope. Often as they made camp they were ill and sat in wet robes which the fire could not dry as it lost its battle to stay alight.

They spent the second night after the rains in the same place, unable to push forward on their journey. In the morning the lay sisters went foraging for sustenance. The earth was soft and treacherous where they stepped but duty made them continue until they were out of sight of their camp. There was nothing to be had for food, and they were not too skilled in trapping the small animals, although they could all skin and gut well enough. Their guide had been the most successful in procuring food for them and they were ashamed to be so dependent; they must have seemed useless men to him.

'Is it pride that forces us on, sisters?' one spoke at last. Two pairs of tired eyes watched her, but nothing was said. Hunger and cold drove them. As long as they were moving they did not succumb to their weaknesses, did not feel them so clearly, and they thought of God and stopped contemplating their discomfort, even if the clothes stuck to their backs and their hands froze.

A sudden, heavy fall of rain stung them. Like a battering ram the sky struck and they were scared to lift their heads but kept them tucked in like pigeons.

'Run to that large rock, we might shelter behind it.' The tallest sister spoke. She covered her head with her arms and looked out. She felt hail striking her skin. It bounced off the bare forearms she held up to protect her face. It dropped like small stones to graze and wound them.

'We cannot stand in this. We must press on to that rock. It might shield us from the worst.'

They tried to run but the earth was softening already. In places pools of mud collected and the ground was turning into liquid. They walked out into a sinking patch and were held fast. Were they alone in such ruin, or was the entire province suffering? Before they started out the weather had been fine; days which were shortening had been cold but clear, good riding weather in which they thought to make steady progress. They did not hesitate or let the darker nights impede them. But had anyone seen signs that such catastrophe waited for them?

They imagined it was peaceful in the lowland. Up here they were alone, the parent house lost to them, and now they were deserted by all living things.

The three shouted, but they knew the party would not hear them. They felt the soft earth grip, they had heard of such things, there were trees which walked like men, earth which pulled souls into it. The soil put out roots to bind and make them part of this plant-life, and the tales of travellers surrounded them. They yelled but their voices were feeble against the continuous deluge which cut them off from all hope. No animal ventured out. In the onslaught the smaller branches broke from trees and crashed to the ground. No footstep or print disturbed the surface of the mud, the instinct of animals had warned those creatures who dwelt here to take to higher ground, and the trees were heavy with every climbing thing. But these three, unprotected by nature and helpless against such savagery, continued to shout until at last their desperate cries were swallowed. The sinking land calmed them with its silence, until there was not a single print left on the surface of the shifting soil.

When the rains abated and the lay sisters still did not return, the party split into three groups. Aelreda and the scribe went one way, the two abbesses another, while the boy went alone.

Aelreda listened for their voices, for the sounds of something moving, praying they did not meet a starved animal instead. The nun who spoke various languages stayed behind, to keep the camp from being destroyed. She shouted at regular gaps so that the search parties might hear the noise and not become lost. But Aelreda was certain that she could not find her way back. The ground was grasping, it clawed at their heels and made it hard to lift their feet.

Aelreda was weary, her back ached again. She forgot what it was to be without pain. On a ledge of rough stone she saw a flat place where the surface had been worn smooth, and it reminded her of the flagstoned floors at Fortitude. She nudged it with her toes, then stood on it. It seemed to tremble. A vibration went through the soles of her feet. Suddenly the stone broke away from the ledge and she was hurtling down a slope, along a rain carved path in the mountain wall.

Aelreda was not aware of anything. When she gained consciousness she did not know where she was. The sky looked different. She had no notion of the length of time she lay in the place, but she felt the gnawing in her belly and, whenever she moved, the blinding flash of pain in her ankle.

Then it was dark again, a darkness she could taste with her tongue's tip, unlike the other darkness she had known which came down suddenly and forced all light out, easing her away from pain and cold. Night settled and slowly her eyes picked out shapes in the squinting dark. Something crashed behind her. She heard the sound of its breathing and then something tearing. In the half light she recognised the halo of white hair.

He took her ankle in his hand. She felt the tremor of pain as he bound it with strips from something he wore.

He fashioned a harness, and in this way, back to back, he dragged her from the slope, and crawled out to the flatter land where Aelreda could look back at the sharp drop.

There were so many questions she wanted to ask. He answered her as best he could with nods and hand movements. She understood that the others were safe. He must have come out alone to look for her. He mimed sleeping, then he flopped his arms, letting them swing loosely without strength.

'Ill?' she asked. 'Are the others ill?'

He nodded.

'Too ill to continue?'

The boy dragged his feet exaggeratedly; the others were too weak to continue. He looked at her intently. She blushed. He knew she was no monk. The boy smiled and shook his head from side to side. Catching her hand, he held it as he knelt, touching his forehead against it. So she blessed him even if the holy ring had gone from her finger.

She lay for many days, praying and fainting with the pain. When she opened her eyes the boy would be there, he brought her what food he trapped, and he took her hand in his hands to let her drink the water he poured for her. Sometimes he applied cold compresses to her forehead, sometimes she would wake up to feel the boy pinning her arms down, then she understood that she had moved in her sleep and he had saved her from greater injury. Once she woke and he was not there. Aelreda thought herself abandoned and began to pray for him. When she heard his footsteps she cried. He came back carrying four small birds over his shoulder. He dropped his burden and grinned broadly, miming how he had caught them as he set about plucking their scrawny bodies.

He had made a shelter for them by overlapping dead branches to form a wind-break. Now he hung feathers from it, pushing them up between the spaces, laughing noiselessly as he did so. He held out an upturned palm of soft, curled white down and she took it from him. He stooped and watched her face. He looked puzzled and slowly put out one finger to touch her cheek. He traced the pale lines of tears. And she was disturbed by his gentleness.

When the abbess could manage to hobble they went towards the camp but found only traces of it. There was no sense in trying to return. It would be safer to travel to the sisters and there rest and gather their strength and hopefully meet with the rest of their party. Aelreda prayed that her sisters would reach the destination safely. A bedraggled delegation they would be, arriving all at different times. But they could stay there until it was safe to return, when the winter had passed its worst. Then they might join a pilgrim party openly, no more secrecy.

To Aelreda survival seemed the root of the expedition, the original quest was far from her thoughts. She cared little for relics as they trudged on through icy paths which stung their feet as shoes split and fell apart.

They came to a tunnel which opened out from a rock face, a natural formation. It was like a cave, only it burrowed back into the earth, and the boy led her along this. She was terrified, but in the dark his hand gripped hers reassuringly. He seemed familiar with the underground place. It felt endless. They crawled along it. In parts it became narrow and they could not stand but slithered like snakes on their bellies. And time was measured differently; by heart-beats and by the number of paters she recited endlessly to keep awake. Here there were no days or nights, but a steady, continuous dark. Although there was no change in the light their eyes began to adjust as those of strange night animals do.

Aelreda wondered if she saw distant shapes, dim figures; but after moving forward they would dissolve as into a dark mist that surrounded everything and, further away, always beyond reach, she would see the outlines re-group ahead of her.

Their exhaustion marked when they should rest. Sometimes she did not know if she slept or was still awake. Nothing marked the sightlessness of the tunnel, or broke the silence as she followed the boy, squeezing into places where it was no bigger than a man's girth. Sometimes it was as if all air had been sucked out and she would choke and try to breathe in panicky little gasps as he pulled her through the narrowest places.

It was like a constant dream, the only sounds those of breathing or the rasp of clothing against walls. Now when she slept her dreams were full of light and colours, and she woke in the dark reality of the tunnel.

Was this one of the routes which would take them inside the

Convent of Compassionate Darkness? Mother Albergisten had hinted that there might be other entrances. There were stories of underground routes which local people knew. Travellers entered through a pilgrims' arch on the north side. That was where she ought to be, not crawling in filth inside the guts of the convent which had been gouged out of earth so that part of it was always buried. But she did not know whether this was it, or whether they were lost, their journey wasted in some endless tunnel.

It seemed as if everything before this had been a dream. Here was reality, the reality of touch. The chafe of her robe, the pull of her belt. The aches deep in her bones and that ankle which would never heal, but throbbed insistently when she was weary.

And she was hot. Sometimes too hot, and she would feel her warm breath around her face as the walls closed in on her at a narrow part where the opening tapered.

He always went ahead, checking and testing the way which he would communicate by a touch on her arm, reassuring with his careful hands. Sometimes she would feel him tracing the shape of her mouth, or her forehead as they lay sleeping. It was as if she did not need words, for by such contact she felt closer to the boy than she had ever been to anyone. Words would get in the way. He knew, as an animal senses fear, what she was feeling. He knew when she could not go on but had to rest. He understood her needs, even those she might never let herself think of.

She prayed continuously for a miracle. She would sacrifice anything.

In a dream a voice had spoken to her. She must sacrifice that which she held dear. She had dedicated herself to blessed chastity. Was it pride that she took in her unblemished body? If so she must offer herself in all humility to her Lord, and let her spiritual chastity ascend to Heaven. Then her body must suffer, it must relinquish its pride, and never give her cause for pride again. She would suffer her mortal self to be exalted in glory, wondering if this was death. For her body had never been used in this way and the boy, like one starved, took it and made use of it as he knew – not gently or knowingly, but clumsily and in ignorance. She shuddered and wept.

10

MANNERS

The Convent of Fortitude. The year of Our Lord 904.

The corporeal state is like a moon, waxing and waning in its creation. The soul descends to human form. It hovers slowly to be infested by woman-state, but for the male it is swift and takes on his shape rejoicing. In some cases as long as one hundred and fifty days for female life to possess a soul; scarce forty for the male has been observed. At these times the mother might feel the soul enter, Scolastica says. From Aristotle she records the menses, that time of losing the foul waste which chooses not to congeal into the shape of life. But God has made us in this state, and so it is that by these pure souls we escape the prisons of flesh.

This day, the Feast of Saint Martin, I have had much talk with Scolastica. By her guidance I study those diagrams she makes, but I fail to understand all I copy. By understanding, the worst mistakes are avoided. This I tell my charges who would work blindly without reason to guide them. Without this, simple errors are magnified.

Not one coming to me this twelve month shows any skill with the pen. They are a gaggle, given to idleness. Obedient enough, but dull.

I am to make a proper work recording the soul's journey, and the body's, to life. Not one inker can I trust but must carry out this task alone. Scolastica instructs me that I shall write all her teaching on the corpus. This we will keep in our library, a great work in progress to please Aelreda when she returns, if God wills it.

And of our beloved abbess we hear no tidings. Much time has passed since she left. Each day reaches into the next. I am called upon little in her absence; praise be, that I might concentrate on the page. Already the lay sisters grind shells in anticipation, and the children prepare the inkstand.

It was one of the worst nights in the nuns' memory. Hail battered on their collective senses, pelted its warning that this long, smothered night was one to fear. The sky was dark. Angry winds came from the east.

Looking out of the scriptorium window, Werberga saw a streak of lightning break the clouds and scatter them. The work in front of her was lit up sharply by the crackling white flash. The burnished gold of the capital shone in glory, the red glowed and the unfinished tiller rested in outline upon his hoe for a brief respite from his labours in shocked sunlight before everything sank back into night. She worked on by the flickering light of a candle.

She counted after each peal of thunder, waiting for the sharp light of the spluttering sky. The brilliance subsided and she worked steadily on the small lettering. But there was a glow, prickly and erratic at first as sun glints on metal, blinding and painful in flashes. The sky brightened to palest grey. She watched; it faded like a wash of ink over a tracing which lets the under-drawing show through, sudden as discovery. But there was no drawing save a mesh of stars as the sky blackened again. From the dark a sudden bladder of fire plunged earthwards trailing brands and flames, then was gone.

She wondered if it was her imagination, seeing designs in heaven when she ought to see them on vellum. She bent over her page hoping no one would interrupt, or ask for her final word on some matter. Decisions had to be made, life must continue without dissent. Only once since Aelreda's departure had she been called on. A dispute in the kitchen had needed the abbess. She prayed that nothing further should upset the running of the convent. But if it did, she knew that she could stand up as well as any other to trouble, or to the interference of monks. She gazed out of the window and her face was illuminated by a sudden flash. Her eyes blazed as she sensed that the period of calm might be drawing to a close.

In the outhouses Scolastica paced the floor. She knew this night was special. As another flash of lightning lit the room she rushed to the window and pulled the shutters open. She watched the sky, counted the silences between each peal of thunder, noting how long they lasted. Both postulants shivered and stood back from the window. There was another great flash. Scolastica's face lit up. It looked white and her teeth glinted in a huge open-mouthed smile.

'Yes! Yes!' she breathed. 'You see it?'

Her finger pointed.

'Watch the sky. Every move. Remember the prophecy is being fulfilled. This is what the old ones spoke about. In the year 906, men will remember the omens.'

As the sky darkened, Scolastica moved to her table and began writing neat rows of columns in a small book, scratching furiously with a black point.

Outside, rain lashed the walls of the outhouses. Hens huddled together. Everything was indoors on such a night; birds sheltered in roofs. A sea tumbled from the sky and in the village men saw fish fall and swim away as sea creatures were loosed upon the earth. And all around there was panic. But the convent was quiet save for the scratching of pens.

The bell rang in the outhouses. Scolastica glanced up from her writing. The public bell.

'Summon the gatekeeper.' She was puzzled for there had been no warning. Whoever arrived that night had crept up in the dark, using it to shield them from the convent's sight.

In the courtyard Agnes, the tallest of the postulants, waited, drawing her cloak about her in the downpour while the gate-keeper, bundled up against the rain, sank deeper into the mud drawing bolts and fumbling. As she located the great lock the only noises were of rust scraping and the constant drumming of rain, perpetual and even-sounding, interrupted by the noise of the heavy key as it bedded in the lock.

The gate turned heavily inwards then stuck. A ridge of earth stopped it. They dug to free it, both postulant and gate-keeper clawing at wet earth. Agnes felt as if she was digging a grave. She scratched the soil. They threw back clods of earth and their backs became wet as the useless cloaks dripped. Agnes felt hers fold about her like night swallowing the sun. It enveloped her, sodden and twice its weight. It dragged and chafed her ankles.

When the gate moved at last they pushed it full circle, and a stranger was admitted to the enclosure. A slow, stately woman with a straight back, who lifted her head proudly and did not hide herself as she climbed down.

Agnes saw that the woman was taller than her. She would have been slender but for her condition. She held herself erect and moved carefully instead of scampering like a rat as the villagers did. She kept easy pace with the postulant, showing no annoyance at the measured walk, made longer and more wearisome by the ritual of procession. She did not attempt to speak. She understood the need for silence.

She stood in the infirmary door with dripping hair. Her threadbare cloak steamed when she was invited to warm herself. A dry robe was brought and Agnes noted of how fine and delicate a weave the old cloak was. Her shoes were ruined, but were of tanned leather and stitched around. Here, Agnes thought, was a noble woman come upon hard times.

Scolastica started immediately. She made up her packets in silence while the woman rested on a wooden pallet.

The woman answered about herself briefly, but asked questions of her own showing that she was a woman of education. Her hands were soft and white with delicate shaped nails. No labourer's wife, this woman without name, but possibly the daughter of a merchant or a noble. All she told them was that she had travelled far. At first she had an ass but it went lame and was abandoned. She travelled on foot with a companion, the same who now waited for her in the village.

Scolastica was accustomed to women who came without their husbands' knowledge, and those who fled before their transgression was discovered. She had grown used to the look of young girls who hid themselves. But this woman had travelled with a man, a man who knew her condition, and took care to bring her to the convent where she might be helped.

'We can't keep our child.'

The woman spoke softly. She was slight so that the loose folds of the robe fell across her belly and all but hid the sign of her fertility. She did not speak until asked a question and then replied with brevity as one accustomed to disciplined speech. Her movements were decorous. When she walked she kept her head bent, raising her eyes occasionally and quickly withdrawing them as if something unpleasant stared her in the face. Her manner and deportment were graceful yet without charm or coyness. She had none of the affectations of wealthy women. She was humble despite her obvious learning and respectful in the presence of Scolastica.

She was vague about times and dates, but she asked much concerning the time of the soul's descent. She had studied Aristotle and wanted to know each detail to secure her own peace and be certain that what she did was no sin, that the fluid was indeed soulless.

For once Scolastica let herself be swayed by the woman's words. She believed what she said in truth and discounted the evidence she saw with her own eyes.

Her belly felt soft although it was swollen, it was not hard or it would be too late to effect any remedy. Scolastica knew that she would have to draw the soulless thing away from the womb; it was past the time for infusions to set off bleeding, too late for those strong mixtures she gave to cause the liquids to spill rather than solidify into wretched life.

The egg sack spun in such a clear circle; the thing in the womb was without spirit. Scarce ten more days and Scolastica would not have been able to alter the course of life.

The old nun watched. Silence and then sudden bells did not startle the woman. Later as the bell for compline sounded the woman thought to follow her to choir and join in the prayers. She sent her back.

'You need rest, for what will take place tomorrow might take all your strength. Go back now to the infirmary and sleep.'

But at sun-rise the next day, when Scolastica remained in her place in the choir for silent prayer, she noticed the woman in the stalls reserved for female visitors. The ordered life of the convent was natural to her, she knew its routine. A born nun, the infirmarian told herself, while her eyes slid down to her belly, reminding her that this woman had not come to them as a novice.

Later that day Scolastica mixed up a very strong infusion of rue. The yellow heads were gatherd in the summer and crushed and dried. There was oil from the same plant. She measured this out carefully into a container and sorted through the bowl counters. She chose the one with five small holes bored through its base. Later when she was ready she would set this into a tub of water, waiting for it to sink while the mixture stood.

Rue was good for purging, but poisonous if wrongfully administered. She knew to treat these things with respect. One pod extra, just a few more seeds than a mixture ought to have, and the result could be death.

Rue congested the organs inside the abdomen, held together by the stern corset of bones. She trusted it as a method. It was miserable and painful in its way, but it should affect a discharge of all matter.

She moved quickly, taking from the cupboard various jars and boxes. She kept the medicines under lock and key because they were a dangerous assortment if they fell into the wrong hands. She kept winter yew needles, at their most virulent in this form, and white hedge hysop which was collected in spring and summer from the swampy places. Each year she would hunt through their outlying fields to where the bog marshes sweated, where the horsetails and yellow flag covered the weeping land.

Carefully she counted out seeds from last winter's hoard. Some she roasted over a flame until they popped. If these were taken entire, swallowed without another balance, they produced strange burning feelings in the eyes and caused the victim to feel the earth twist. They might see men walking on their sides; all was distorted as through a piece of curved glass.

Scolastica took down the jar where she stored the henbane. This was a good reactor; misused it sent people mad. From the induced flights of fancy few were known to return. Those that did had been in Hell with all its horrors. They stared, drooling as lunatics. She had been taken to see henbane sickness once. A family, all touched by madness. With sudden violence any of them might lash out, fighting as if they were Satan's legion. They were all restrained in some fashion, their arms fastened to posts or chained up. The mother had a strong branch hanging down her back and the grandfather lay, secured to a flat board for his own safety. He cackled and spat. A terrible memory.

She looked for the dried bundles of last season's hemlock. She crushed the brownest parts from the clustered heads and measured the amount along her finger nail. Better to use too few. A tiny amount to calm a frantic mind.

She locked the cupboard carefully behind her. At the fire she began to prepare the medicine. She took another timing bowl and set this in the barrel. Water began to pour through slowly. When it had filled level with the second line drawn inside, she removed the mixture from the heat and left it to cool. She heard the bowl knock against the bottom of the barrel as it sunk.

The door opened. The novices brought the woman through. She appeared very distressed this time, crying and glancing round the room. Everything seemed to fill her with fear, now it was the time.

She was nearly at the limit of the days, well into the last stage according to Scolastica's reckoning. But the egg sack had been certain. There was no danger.

While the Little Sister of Poverty helped the woman to lay back on the pallet, Scolastica heated a metal rod in the fire, saying prayers over it and blowing with bellows until it glowed. Then she plunged it into a basin of water. Steam hissed and she made the sign of the cross. It had been cleansed in fire, no hand would touch the spike, no fingers defile it.

The novices covered the patient with a thick woollen blanket to keep her warm. She drank the infusion and looked troubled.

Scolastica knew that there would be only a sign of blood-letting, because this child, although soulless, would cling to its shape.

Carefully she inserted the metal pin high inside the ripe body; the woman moved and she hissed at her to lie still. The poor thing could not endure the sickness and moaned, threshing with her arms.

'Hold her down,' Scolastica ordered and the two novices pinned her on either side to the hard frame.

Scolastica's hand shook, and she prayed that she would locate the ridge and lump, like a textural map. She felt the right place and punched with the metal pin. She felt something tear and carefully withdrew the piece of steel. Water rushed out and some blood, as when the centurions pierced the side of Christ.

'Make another infusion, lots of arrowroot and liquorice to ease her muscles and hemp for pain,' she ordered. 'Anoint her lower half, with hazel and lavender. Under her nose put the likes of bitumen or sulphur, the foulest smell so that the matter is drawn down towards the relief of scent.'

While Agnes went to the cupboard and took down rock

cedar to prepare an infusion, the other burnt goat's hair and hartshorn. She held this to her nose. The woman gagged and retched, but they told her to breathe deeply from it and would not take it away but forced her face down into it.

Scolastica watched. This was nothing to what she would endure before the day ended, before her raw womb was left gaping. She pitied yet dreaded this woman; something about her disturbed Scolastica. Then she noticed that where the cloth fell from her shoulders, the woman's skin was pitted with scars, tiny little cuts. Where the marks were oldest they were thick and ridged, layers of obligatory suffering. Her own shoulders were just like this from the flails. The stranger's shoulders were as numb as any ritualist's.

What followed was the hardest purging Scolastica had performed. The woman screamed and writhed and the old nun was powerless to ease her. The infusions she made had no effect. Pain was obligatory.

Scolastica gritted her teeth, prayed that it would pass quickly, while the poor creature shouted that God was punishing her, that she deserved this. Scolastica remained with her and would not leave her throughout the worst pain, but experienced it with her, and wished there was a way of taking it from her.

The woman called out as waves of pain dragged her into despair, and at last her strength broke and she begged Scolastica to do something. The old nun spoke harshly.

'Did you think it would be easy?'

It must be borne, and she turned her head away. Scolastica measured the lulls in the rhythmic tides of the stranger's body, counting as for one in childbed. Then a strong surge forced the woman low on the pallet. She was grunting like an animal, reduced to that speechless state Scolastica had seen in so many. Now was the time.

The postulants took positions at the end of the bed. The woman lay on her back and they waited. Then she screamed as the soulless creature spewed from between her legs a burst of blood and fluid. She was very still; she moaned, not fully conscious. At least she had that relief.

On the wooden slats the cord glistened. There was no movement in it, a good sign. The old nun waited then gently tugged and the dark mushroom holding the coiled rope came free, blistered and wet and still attached to the shape. This Godless one clung to human form, it parodied life with its small hands and feet.

Scolastica would put the body into one of the lidded baskets they used to transport these to outside the wall where a village woman collected. Usually she did not look. The outpourings were formless, unrecognisable. This one was lying with its arms crossed over its chest, accidentally, as it had fallen, but it gave it the attitude of prayer. And she saw then that it was male.

She heard a screech in the courtyard, and the sky was still and attentive. Her face contorted in anguish. Her assistants, busy with clearing up, both felt a chill. Their teacher was frightful in appearance; she shook violently. What had happened?

And then they knew that the signs had been wrong. This was no soulless one, they had been deceived. There was a long silence, they might never speak again, but Scolastica forced herself to break it.

'Let none speak of this ever,' her voice was low and steady. Her mind raced to interpret what had happened. She had been misled. She fastened the lid of the basket tightly, so that none might look inside. She glanced at the woman, and seeing that she was still unconscious, quickly made the sign of the cross.

'We have witnessed the work of great evil, masquerading as good. The eggs were wrong; the hen that laid them has been taken over by an evil spirit using its form. The hen-house harbours the Devil.' She strode out.

The next morning when the kitchen sisters went to gather eggs, they came running back.

'Mercy on us Lord!' one exclaimed, entering with an empty basket.

'Every hen has had its neck wrung, all there is left is the rooster, it crowed three times, I swear I heard it crow three times. Someone among us has betrayed Jesus!

11

POISON

THE DYING AND THE almost dead were left outside their walls. Often they would nurse someone whose family had cast them out to avoid contagion. In times of plague they sealed the gate to keep the ravages out, but many a one thinking themselves healthy threw themselves against this, imploring to be allowed to enter where they might avoid the dreadful spreading sickness.

Many fists would bang against those gates. The sisters became deaf to the pleas in times of dearth, for they did not have enough for themselves, and the survival of their community was their chief concern. Who would give them charity if they were forced to leave their convent? Who would nurse them if one after another they were to die? If they were to open the gates then the villagers would flee.

In times of health they would take in sick women, and do whatever they could. But they knew that the outsider who was among them had come to die.

None had seen her enter save the gate-keeper and one postulant, but they trusted Scolastica to do all she could. Yet the woman was wasting. She had been talking for they heard her voice as they passed the outhouses, but in the following days, Scolastica with all her knowledge could not make potions fast enough to stop the woman's energy ebbing. Then the woman could not utter a sentence. She faded gradually, her pale skin became transparent and a map of blue veins could be read in her neck as she sank further into unconsciousness.

The order prayed for her, and for the safe return of their abbess. Prayers endlessly offered up without a sign that they had been heard. The woman did not improve, and they had no news of Aelreda.

In the outhouse the woman bled. The Little Sister of Poverty and Agnes packed out the bed with clean straw, threw sawdust on the floor to absorb it, but the blood would not stop. It welled up like a fountain and her life ran out of her. Scolastica was powerless.

The postulants knew that she would have borne a son had the matter been left uninterrupted. A fine strong boy he might have been, a pope. The woman believed she had been rid of the soulless. Her eyes blazed with fever. She was ready to join the other world and face damnation, but she did not know it. The two who attended her were too frightened to utter the truth.

'A community,' she whispered, 'we were going to found a community. My brother in Christ was expelled for loving me. We thought to travel north and begin a simple foundation, with men and women together. Then this, because of our earthly and carnal desire. But I was a devout sister . . . he was my bridegroom in God, he was my bridegroom on earth as God might still be mine in Heaven . . .'

They did all they could to make her passage from life comfortable, and wept. She would be denied eternal life through their fault. As her head fell to one side, they remarked how she expired gently, like a born nun.

'She has returned to Christ then?' deaf Sister Martha asked, for she had not heard the rattle calling the order to prayer. The postulants were silent, but Martha thinking they replied, continued on her way to the mill-house.

The postulants could feel the evil being among them. Evil roamed the walls, attempted to climb in through the turn-gate. It had been there the night that the gate, sensing the terrible presence, had refused to open. It stuck into muddy earth in an attempt to stay their hands. Agnes had forced the gate, had dug, had sweated and worked to move it. She was part of the awful chain of events. She was to blame, she let evil into the convent. There were plenty of signs that night. They were warned, but neither of them paid heed.

The postulants could not understand how their teacher was wrong. Their mentor had failed, her calculations were inaccurate and they had assisted in murder. The blood of the innocent would be forever on them. And the knowledge that they had caused a soul to be damned, for it was unbaptised.

'Did it breathe, was it seen to breathe?' Agnes asked, but the Little Sister shook her head. No baptism could have been wished. The soul had already begun its descent, and no phrase could recall it.

The Little Sister had wanted too much science, too much learning. She thought that she could understand the mysteries of life, but now she saw that it was pride, and the work of the Devil.

'We are living through dangerous times,' Scolastica told them. She consulted her charts.

'Are we witnessing the first days of the world's death?' the Little Sister of Poverty asked. But Scolastica shook her head.

'A sacrifice was made,' she said. 'A sacrifice that was not intended. An unbaptised soul is gone. And I was clear in my heart that this was a soulless child. Unwittingly I sent it to the Devil. The packets lied, the Evil One pulled them, spun them into deceitful circles. Foul spirits are here, and I was used by them.'

She paced back and forth. Suddenly she stopped and drew one finger up.

'I must make it impossible for those powers to use me as an instrument. They will not be able to pull me and make me do their bidding.'

She turned to face her two students.

'Sisters, your hearts are pure. You must continue for me, you will be my hands. I shall direct you from where nothing can force my hands to act against God's work. Take my place, between you keep the skills and pass them down. I must take new vows. That's how it can be done . . .'

She turned to look at them with something that resembled a smile. It was indecent on her face.

'I will leave you but still be with you. There is a way . . . why didn't I think of it before?'

The two novices stared helplessly at each other. Agnes opened her mouth as if she might ask a question, but instead said nothing.

'I shall become an anchorite. I shall ask that a cell be made near the altar so that I might watch mass. I should no longer attend it. But this way I can spend my remaining days in atonement.'

The postulants were scared. Without Scolastica they would be tutorless. They would become the repositories of all her theories. Alone, they feared that they could not keep the learning alive. They doubted their will, as much as their ability. They had seen how her ideas could be wrong. Their certain world had been shaken and they lost their appetite for knowledge.

When the strange woman died, the convent mourned. The order knew of no illness, yet Scolastica had not been able to save her. They puzzled over this and attributed to it the change which came over the old nun. None were surprised when shortly afterwards she announced her decision to take further vows and devote the rest of her days to silence and prayer. They thought her skills had deserted her, and wondered who would act as their infirmarian.

Werberga began to hire workers for digging; the cell was to be sunk into the chapel floor. Dug out like a well, the walls were to be lined with stone. It would be deep enough for Scolastica to stand in, her head level with the chapel floor, and it would be raised and roofed over with a metal grille at the front so the anchorite could look out. It would appear like a small platform, and be near the altar. The nun could still hear mass on the women's side.

In preparation for this Scolastica began to spend much of her time alone. This was why she did not attend the rites over the grave for the woman. Instead she paced alone in the cloisters, while within the reilig na mban, where none but nuns might lie, they placed the remains of the one she had been unable to save.

A born nun she had been, and now she returned to stay amongst them. She had suffered enough for one man in her life, and Scolastica agreed with the rest of the order when they remarked how it felt correct to lie her down in the earth where no man might set foot. And she prayed that God would be merciful.

The Convent of Fortitude. The Year of Our Lord 904. The mass day of Sisinnius the Martyr.

Into our silent world the hirelings were herded as terrified animals. Warned to observe silence they went about their task without speech or story to relieve the tedium, but as dusk fell and they were shown out, their raucous shouts did disturb our sisters from thoughts of God.

We gave them our blessing in token, and their fill of food. But some contrived by lewd gesture and sign to convey their basest urges, that which makes man no better than a beast. Our youngest entrants were kept head down in the cloisters, and so exhausted with memorising new verses for the chant at choir they scarce had time to witness the men who grunted like swine and fell upon their food. Let no women glance towards their bellies for increase. No help is to be given.

Our Sister Scolastica remains daily in her own company, and food is sent to her. It is only a matter of time before the cell is completed then she will joyously take her new vows. Every day brings her nearer to her desire. I am not to work on the manuscripts, for Scolastica is troubled and they are taken from me. She only desires to be interred to pray continuously for our order, blessed be her words.

Next came masons and cutters with white quarried stone. The chip and chink of hammers filled the convent as they cut grooves and bevelled corners to edge the pieces, splashing from metal buckets to work on wet stone. They marked the load bearing stones with lozenges, for each man makes his own mark, which will last for ever so all might know his skill. Squat blocks are pushed along ramps to line the gaping pit the hirelings dig.

The free hand carver we asked to cut a design for two top panels to show Christ's triumph over death. But the abbot could not agree a price so we have arranged a simpler work with no figures. Now he cuts devices to look like nature; stone plants and leaves surround the top.

The mason cuts his way to everlasting life, sweating in the afternoon in his shirt for modesty. His perspiration hits the stone's surface in blots, stains the white birds and flowers that twist from his skilled hands.

In the courtyard there is a pile of this smooth stone, and ropes and other things used for lowering and carrying. It is good white stone which the workers left and we could return it and so reduce our debt, but the abbot, preaching for our safety and in such haste to bless and re-sanctify the ground did cause us to seal up the double doors earlier than we might.

He cleansed our side with holy water and walked backward to wipe away those marks left by his feet. So the floor is washed of all men's tread. And now the edges to the door are sealed with the dark wax as is proper.

Our order settles back into calm, and Scolastica is peaceful inside the new, barred cell.

In the convent there were those who thought their abbess was dead, but none said as much. No news reached them and they wondered what had happened on the journey to the parent house. They waited for messages but none came. At last they agreed that she might have perished and they felt that they ought to make plans for the future running of Fortitude without her.

None prayed more fervently for the abbess's return than Werberga. Each day she waited for a messenger who would bring her a letter. She dreaded that letter, for it might tell them what they all suspected. But then they would have to hold a re-election and she would be able to stand down as acting head. She prayed that she would not be given the duty if it arose.

Scolastica was nervous. Everything she had worked for would be lost unless she could guarantee her students' efforts. The abbess would have made sure that they continued to progress, but Werberga could not make such decisions. Under her everything was in a state of uncertainty. Her power was temporary. Scolastica would have to issue her own instructions.

'You must continue the work.' That was her first instruction. Her voice was slow and steady. The two postulants looked towards the sound but could not make out the speaker's form in the darkness of the cell. They peered down through the bars and felt the cold rush of air where they knelt.

The anchorite's head was level with the ground, her cell sunken into the earth. She stood pressed up to the stone wall, her voice rasped against the silence in the church. Long fingers wrapped around the bars, closing on them in a tight grip. They squeezed the metal and the muscle in her arms tensed, until she had exhausted herself on the barren act of strength.

That night the yellow half-moon was masked in shadows and vapour, giving a thin, watery light which made everyday things grotesque, their details picked out like deformities. The postulants' faces shone with the pallor beyond death that brings with it the darkening touch of decay. It was as if both were caught before the impending end of all living things, to which they knew they should come, yet were held for a moment in brilliant, corpse-white gleam. They had surrendered their chance of immortality.

Their eyes peered in the gloom. They wanted advice, they came for instruction; they were used to following orders, they could not continue without their teacher. Even as she proved fallible, they returned to ask for guidance.

Hearing the hand rub against the bars, both prostrated themselves on the stone flags. They threw out their arms in the shape of the cross and turned their faces painfully towards the cell on a level with the anchorite's face. Now they saw her watery eyes glisten as gradually they became accustomed to the dark and when she spoke the occasional glint of weak moon would pick out a single tooth.

'Between you there is knowledge which you can develop. It will help you and all womankind. You must continue. Watch for signs. Search the sky. Examine it for the messages that those with their heads bent praying can never see.

'Walk upright, your eyes toward the clouds. Your task is to warn others. Untrained eyes cannot read impending disaster. You can forewarn; and so you must.'

Agnes and the Little Sister of Poverty watched, each wanting to know what the other thought. They had come in a spirit of penitence, wanting to atone for all wrongs. This was not what they imagined they would hear.

'Pray for me, you who have made no mistakes, whose hands have not been led to sin. Ask God for His forgiveness for I alone am guilty,' the voice of their teacher told them.

They both shuddered and Agnes raised herself to kneel, burying her head in her hands. The other remained flat, but dropped her head and made no effort to look towards the cell's bars. She lay without moving.

The speaker did not sense her pupils' reactions.

'I leave you all my writings and ask you to use them well. Observe and note. Never speak of that night. I have been given a sign that I am no longer to practise, but you will carry the teaching beyond me. Such knowledge must be passed to others. Even if your hearts knock inside you and you tremble to use the skills, continue. Teach until there are others willing to take up where we left off.'

'But how, without you to show us? Why, we might make worse crimes by our ignorance, blind as new born mice. We have not the understanding.'

Scolastica's voice cracked in desperation, this was her final edict and she would be obeyed. Her voice smacked its authority to her wayward pupils. But it was flawed, the speaker mortal.

'I am guilty alone,' she said. 'You have made no mistake.'

This was what they could not comprehend; Scolastica, who knew everything and was wiser than anyone had been at fault. An error of judgment turned her away from Heaven, made her unsaintly. Their earth rocked, their belief in order shook.

Scolastica forced her arms between the bars. Her long fingers groped and caught the top of the young sister's head, as she lay stretched without energy or will to move. The novice recoiled at the touch and pulled back sharply. Scolastica was pointing with her long fingers. Agnes, hearing the rapid movement, lifted her face and saw her teacher's hand stretched towards the outhouses. Then it slowly withdrew into the shadow of the cell, where they heard her voice asking them to pray for her. Then silence.

In the weeks that followed, the convent became concerned about the two. Werberga listened to complaints that they spent too much of their time together. There was anxiety if anyone in the order was too frequently in another's company, for this made them less equal as companions to the others; and so they were to spend their time without favouritism for another sister. Werberga feared that the two postulants were growing as close as blood-sisters. Attempts were made to split them, but as their orders were to continue Scolastica's work in the infirmary, it was impossible to devise times when their labours would not bring them together. Werberga was not able to go against Scolastica's wishes, even when she saw how the two sisters were behaving. In choir their positions were changed so that they might not stand next to each other, but despite such measures they clung together, abandoned as orphans.

Werberga did not know what to recommend in the abbess's place. She tried to discipline them and bring them gradually into line. Only the day before she had made them both beg their bread in the refectory, going around the table in humility after the rest had eaten. Today she made them kneel throughout the meal and only rise after the others had left, and so she punished them for their sin of companionship.

Werberga could not prohibit them from learning; that was part of their vocation. There was no restructuring of the day possible. The main work hours were between sext and none and only by missing the daily office could the routine be varied. But Werberga's actions had little effect. Their terrible secret drew them together, despite Scolastica's assurances that they were innocent.

All the convent saw how they worked without rest. The two could be heard disputing fiercely. They had frenzied arguments about dates and times and the displacement of souls. They talked round in circles each time, and they believed that they too were denied the light of God.

Agnes had troubled dreams. She dug endlessly recalling the odd sensation that she was digging a grave. She would wake roughly and sit upright, her hands flat like spades, palms turned upwards. Her fingers pushed through holes in the worn coverlet.

On those nights her entire body ached and then she felt that she, who had no experience of men, bore the child of the strange woman. It was punishment. Sweating as one in childbed, she would find in the morning the sign of blood on the rough cover. She suffered for her sin as the horrific dream repeated itself.

The Little Sister of Poverty made foul mixtures and drank them to atone for her wrong. The mixtures grew worse and stronger as the Little Sister hoped they might lessen her mortal time of suffering. She passed them to Agnes and it became a ritual of mortification as they drank from the solution, believing that the fouler it was the better it paid for their misdeed.

They grew suspicious of Scolastica's teaching, mistrusted words upon the page. There was no one to answer their questions and without guidance the postulants sank. They were outside the ordinary running of the house. At each meal they knelt alone.

They mixed soda ash and quicksilver, made infusions with mercury, soaked roots in lime and brewed infusions hoping to blind themselves so that they might never have to witness the signs hidden in clouds. Slowly they poisoned themselves and their eyes saw marks and scenes of such squalor.

Agnes saw a tree full of maggots, bloated as after feasting on a corpse; the Little Sister stood under it and it dripped blood. If the sky turned to fire it would not have been sufficient to rouse them for there could be no greater horrors than the ones in their minds.

The convent went about its business not seeing the evil that the postulants knew was deep in its core. Agnes wanted to excavate the evil.

'Help me dig it out Sister,' she asked her companion and her red eyes burned.

At night they made a hole by the chapel wall. Deeper and deeper they dug until they were exhausted. They collapsed into the pit they created and had not the energy to climb out.

It was Werberga who found both sisters clinging together, filthy and bloodied, their faces scratched. The community did not know what to do and they watched the two sisters helplessly.

Together they carried each other deeper into despair, the foul stench of corruption and decay followed them and they could not free themselves.

'All food is waste,' Agnes told one of the kitchen sisters.

She stood on the tiled floor in bare feet. The large nun kept chopping vegetables, roots and turnip heads.

'All sustenance is sinful.'

On hearing this the big nun swung the blade down upon the block with more effort than she needed.

'What is the point of food? Why perpetuate the foul life of the body?' Agnes preached to the nun's back. The big woman made no reply. Like others she believed that Agnes had become the instrument of the Devil; he was using her to spread evil through the convent in this time of unrest. Her lips moved slowly in prayer.

'And don't tell me to look towards Heaven,' the postulant continued. 'What is there in Heaven? Nothing. I look at the sky and at night the stars spark like eyes in rotting fish heads. All the things you labour with every day in the kitchen . . . the smell of offal and the reek of death everywhere.'

The big nun glanced over her shoulder to see Agnes standing next to the heavy container with all the waste that was used for the pigs. She started to roll off the great stone cover.

'Don't!' she shrieked, but Agnes had moved it, with incredible strength, and the sour stink filled the kitchen. Then with a scream of delight the postulant ran out.

Werberga listened to the complaints patiently. Punishing them had no effect. Somehow they would have to be restrained, but before Werberga could give instructions for this, something happened which made such measures unnecessary. One night neither arrived for vespers. Oda, the librarian, was sent to look for them. She went straight to the outhouses. As she opened the door, all was silent and at first she could not see. She carried a torch and thrust it in front of her, holding it high. The infirmary was unrecognisable. Everything had been spilled or moved or rearranged with frantic activity. Bottles lay open on the floor. Gone was the pristine order which Scolastica imposed, clearing away after each working time, as everything went back on to shelves. Her foot brushed against something. Bending down to shake it off she saw that it was a page. The floor was littered with pieces of manuscript. Over in the furthest corner she saw them.

They were huddled together, surrounded by the loose pages of their teacher's writing. Somehow they had managed to get the unfinished book from the library, for that too was on the table. The librarian saw that it had not been set upon yet; their destruction had still to reach it. She picked it up, terrified that anyone should discover that she had been lax and someone had been in the library without her knowledge. She lifted the lid of a coffer and slipped it down inside. She would take it back at the first chance and keep it locked up.

The two sisters were coughing, unable to move. In the light cast by the torch they looked green. The librarian ran shouting to choir where the assembled nuns waited.

Werberga had the two put to bed, and took over the duties of infirmarian without any discussion or election. She did not have time to sanction each new move while Aelreda was away from them, and the sisters were relieved that Werberga gave instructions.

Werberga sat up with them, but then fell into exhausted sleep. At dawn as the rest of the order finished matins, they were found cold and unmoving. After lauds, Werberga went to the cloisters to take up the great wooden rattle. She held it then let it drop. She knew, as many of the others suspected, that there was no purpose in praying for them. They died without repenting, with no one to hear their confession or administer rites.

At the first break from night-fasting, Werberga announced their deaths. An old nun began to speak the Exultet of Saint Ambrose, but a sharp look from another stopped her. Some of the nuns were confused and a lay sister let drop the big metal spoon she carried to table. It clattered on the tiled floor.

Werberga motioned them to sit and beckoned to the reader to take her place at the lectern. The meal began. Only the slow reading and the scrape of metal bowls upon wood disturbed the silence of the refectory. All appeared calm around the table, but each member of the community was in turmoil. But their questions could not break the silence which followed prime.

It was decided to bury the two outside the enclosed cemetery in plain linen shrouds – not in their habits, but in shifts such as workers might use. They were tended quietly by a lay sister and without ceremony or mark of any kind. Their remains were interred outside the low walls of the reilig na mban where the stranger had been buried. Their act of self destruction removed them for ever from God's mercy.

A few weeks after the informal burials Werberga, making an inventory of the infirmary, discovered that quantities of powdered hemlock and quick silver were missing.

Scolastica had to be informed of their deaths. Werberga, with misgivings, sent Gertrude. The kindly nun returned saying how the anchorite shrieked aloud on hearing such tidings.

But Scolastica did not stop at a shriek. She was agitated. A righteous fervour now burned inside her. She would defeat the Devil. She broke her self-imposed silence and once again began to teach, this time to an empty chapel so that the stones might hear her wisdom and carry her message. The knowledge she had would not dry up inside her. Like a stream she would let it flow away from her, so that it might reach to all living things. When they came to pray they heard her words, whispered softly on the first wave of singing, and their voices rose to God and drowned her out. But her message spread, as though it was taken in the air. Women came seeking instruction, and to pray, but the turn-gate no longer let them enter. Even to sit at Scolastica's feet was now considered too great a risk.

12

COMPASSION

THE SISTERS OF COMPASSIONATE Darkness communicate by touch with fingertips sensitive as stamens left to quiver after the bee dusts the blossom. Such fingers sprout like snail horns; uncurl and hang on air, caressing sound. They glow with nerves. This way they register change in the world. They know when it rains, when it thunders. They know by the tingling of their fingers when moisture is carried on the spores and seeds to new life.

In the depths of earth they dispense with words, but their ears pick up sounds lost to all others. Warm air presses upon their faces. Speech eats air, it is wasteful. They remember the air-eaters who live above them. Once they went among them, but now their eyes sting in daylight. They are almost blind. They go swiftly on all fours in places where the underground passages narrow to the girth of a child and they move with certainty through the long winding tunnels of their sunken abbey. Underground they are small and fast. They run full pelt yet seldom collide, moving jerkily to miss an obstacle. They feel the pull and swoop of air, the sudden change. Air is heavy where it surrounds, finer where it disperses after movement. It settles like dust.

Darkness is their penance for their one great ecstasy. Long ago they chose a supernatural light which is locked behind solid doors. In this one room they shield all the light of their hope. Stopped up, pure. They do not squander it, nor let it seep weakly into darkness. A brilliant pinhead of illumination in a world of shadows.

Their moment comes when they are pierced with brightness. Their eyes stabbed with radiance. They call it merely a glimmer of his beauty. Outside this room the torch lighters sleep pressed against the walls of the widening chamber. In turn, they guard the door. They keep the flame burning which ignites all the torches and candles in the room of light. They were brought in as children and remain at the centre of the underground abbey, their tongues cut so talk would not disturb air. Led once into the centre and left there, none have ever found the way back. Only the trusted deal silently with pilgrims, those surface dwellers who enter by the north side where the building is raised from the earth and where slitted windows let in weak streams of day. The enclosed nuns never venture to that part. They stay within the convent's bowels, daylight never bathes them.

Their eyes are pale. Fingers twitch. Something moves. A noise. A stranger has come among them.

Who has entered their dark side? Who moves slowly on the ground? Listen. More than one. How many are there?

Outsiders have found this place.

They wait. The strangers crawl closer. They hear singing, snatches of plainsong. Their ears hurt. A shadow comes towards them. It is not human. Feel how dense the air is now. It speaks. Air races away.

It is human.

They cannot understand its words. Scratching the air they listen. What comes so close to their centre, crawling out of earth? Who can be here, if it is not one of them? They do not move. They wait, silent as burial.

Aelreda crawled. She was too weary to go further, and now she let the boy go ahead. He made the openings wider to give her an easier passage. But the silent ones heard him. The boy banged against something and was seized. Bird claws gripped his shoulder, his mouth was stopped with something – clay or pellets, dry and dusty. Choking, he was dragged away by creatures to another place, pulled through black tunnels until they pushed him into a chamber where he could stand upright.

The torch lighters watched him curiously in the glinting light from their tapers. They fed him and turned away from him. Lay sisters took him in dusk to a place where a high roof rose above him. Blue light crept in through narrow windows and he felt chill air touch his skin and rejoiced to let it fill his weakened lungs. He was left at a pilgrims' arch. He was uninvited. They were not responsible for his safety.

But there was something else still moving inside their sunken abbey. Slowly, awkwardly, a great solid mass disturbed the air. It sang hymns. Sharp, high sounds. They knew that life moved inside it. They heard it turn in the womb. It was female, this creature who came upon them, and because they were women, they relented and took pity on the stranger. They offered her the darkness until her time came.

And so Aelreda was made comfortable. Her strength returned slowly. She remembered why she travelled to the order, but had lost the holy ring and had no seal to show them who she was and, because of her predicament, she was grateful. She begged to see the relic and was finally allowed to follow them into the room whose heavy doors were always tightly shut.

Her eyes had become unaccustomed to light. They watered as she watched the Sisters of Compassionate Darkness who were usually so fast and sure-footed. Here they stumbled and tripped. Light tortured them and they flapped like trapped birds who had flown in through rafters, and crashed about squealing. Their eyes rolled with one burning vision which pushed them to madness. In its orbit they bumped against each other, careered and screeched like wounded gulls.

In every crevice of the shrine candles burned. Shiny metal and silver coins set into the walls reflected light; tiny pieces of glass and mirrors caught it. Copper sheets hung from the roof to magnify the flames. The sharp edges of broken glass sparked like jewels. Colour rippled across her hand.

The sisters clutched their hearts. That was how they knew the points of light had entered their souls. The light cut them, painful in its intensity and they cried out. But Aelreda felt only soft light, and space, as her eyes stopped stinging. In this room she could at last walk like proud man, in this room they were not crawling things. She stretched her spine and felt her great firm belly. She smiled. She was powerful.

In front of the heavy door hung layers of curtains. Aelreda could not be sure how many overlapped each other, she tried to count as she was taken through. These stopped light escaping into the passage ways when the great door was opened, although some always escaped to sprinkle the tunnels. In the room an enormous window was cut out of the solid rock wall. High up, it looked directly at the sky and was filled with marvellous glass and lead work of miraculous quality. Clear yellow and green, the thick glass pieces reflected the rays of the sun, designed to bounce light to every corner.

The torch-lighters ran swiftly between the stacks. They reset candles, wrapped tapers and kept the flames burning. As soon as one went out they lit another, and went busily without a moment's rest.

The heat rose upward into the high ceiling and the air was heady with burning. The sound of breathing was loud and regular. Their eyes spun and some fainted, plunging themselves back into life-giving darkness.

High on a stand was the reliquary. The girdle was kept in a casket of fine metal work, of gold with precious stones. In roundels the length of the box were scenes from the life of Mary. Some depicted her girlhood, the rest the nativity. There were scenes with her mother Anne, and her sister, scenes of such beauty that the casket itself was proclaimed a miracle by all who saw it.

On the feast day of Our Lady the girdle was brought out for the nearest local community and venerated. A Frankish queen had once asked for the right to wear the girdle during her own pregnancy and been refused. They alone had the power to do as they chose with it. And they chose to keep it circled by light, the light of their saviour who burst forth upon the world after the blessed darkness of Mary's womb.

The abbess was shocked by such brilliance and noise. She put out her hand to touch the casket, and as she did so all became dark.

She awoke inside the tunnel. Terrible pains caused her to writhe. Their voices were soft and whispering. They crouched around her and spoke to her in darkness so she might know she was not alone. They stroked her, touched her hand and bathed her face. They stayed with her throughout and gave what help they could. And at the sound of a tiny cry, Aelreda heard their laughter, the sound of their relief.

The saints' days followed each other and Aelreda wondered if she would see the surface again. The air brought in different smells from outside and she longed to be up there. When the sky beyond the window was lightening and the mornings softer, they came to bind her weeping breasts and she understood it was so she might journey from them.

Carrying the child, she would re-enter the world. In her heart was a secret pride for she had seen the Virgin's suffering, she had shared her experience. In the tunnels she heard whispering, her ears keen. They would not cross the main part of the abbey, not appear to the narrow morning light which bled through there.

The lay sisters took her to the raised part of the abbey and at the pilgrims' arch touched her shoulder lightly before turning away. She stepped out, her eyes hurt and she saw her child's face for the first time.

And she thought about the boy who had disappeared from her life as easily as he had been brought into it. He vanished without trace. The lay sisters could not say what had happened to him. They let her know that it was better to forget everything. But as she watched the baby with its pale skin and tufts of white hair her memory was intact. It was one thing no one could take from her.

The baby cried lustily. Aelreda held it to her and walked on, the pilgrims' arch behind her.

The boy had no story to tell. In his home he was given up for dead. The boy's father stopped calling for payment at the Convent of the Crown of Thorns after the first winter. The lay sister waited at the porch every Friday. And then one day an unknown man rode out to her. His hair was hidden under a broad brimmed hat, but she recognised his silence as they had in the village where once there had been a man with a son who never talked.

Neither parent waited for his return, instead he found a rough cross outside the church, and he re-entered the place which they said was his and took rightful possession of it. It was damp and no fire had been lit for a long time. On the table he pushed forgotten bowls aside and his hand tangled in the sticky cobwebs that smothered the empty dishes. He counted the money from the purse the sister gave him. And he cried, looking at the coins spread on the dusty table.

13

BYLOCATION

The Convent of Fortitude. Collop Monday, the Year of Our Lord 905.

Such terrible miseries. There are ill times when divers things unnatural do pass among us. I hesitate to let my pen inform this page, blanched and innocent, to be sullied by words which cannot be spoken.

Scolastica they say was often seen abroad while her body rested in the deep cell. As a phantasm she was seen first by lay sisters, but they, being the more susceptible, were put hard to work so their idle minds would not be led into sin.

Then others saw her in different places and it went around the convent that she did walk right out of her cell. The kitchen sisters would not follow the cellarist, nor help to carry anything but said there was a creature down there.

On Samthann's Day last, she was in the garden they say, where she stood as one carved on the great portals of a cathedral. She did not move. And the shape was not yet solid, but as a shadow through which light might pass. The prickly leaves behind her were showing through the hem of her robe. For she casts out like a reflection on a lake then is gone as quickly as a stone breaks the water's surface.

Scolastica woke in her dark hole. Sweat soaked her as though she had ceased from hard manual work. It dried icily and she shivered with the tiny rivulets of cold. She drew up her knees to hug her skinny flanks and rocked from side to side. For a long while she sat this way in the timelessness which surrounded her. So she remained, spent and exhausted. As she drew in air her lungs shuddered and moved like bellows, unused to such great gasps. She breathed with pain as air slashed like a sword entering her body in swathes and felt the short gasp of the dagger as it was buried to its hilt in her ribs. Slowly did she learn to breathe again and she heard her clouting heart.

In the dark she touched her face and neck, moved her hands over her shoulders and pressed with her palms. She searched the solid state which sprung back, resisting her probing fingers as they felt for any gaps just as Thomas sought the wound in his master's side; but unlike him, she found none. Yet she was certain that this time something had been wrenched from her body.

Each time she returned to it, it felt as if more had been pulled away from the core. She was being flayed like an ear of wheat. She knew how fleeting was this state called corpus. It was ready to change at any time. It was her will that made her return to it because she needed the solid matter called Scolastica, for this was how she was recognised.

She kneaded the wall of her body. Her skin was taut, drawn over a framework of bone. Age did not let her soften. She felt her shoulder joints, rolled them backwards and forwards and felt that everything was as she had left it. Safe in her cell no one could disturb the husk she shed to move weightlessly across the day. She stood on the border of night when it changed to slow morning. Time pushed her forward with a circular movement, returning from dark to day, repeated in every red sunrise as the glowing sphere is born from heaving night and the new risen sun in a bloodied sky bears the criss-crossed sweat streaks on its belly.

She saw life dissolve and rise as vapour. Once she studied the behaviour of elements, let water boil to see how long it took to peck the surface. Steam ran back to water, full-circle. The world went back to back. Everything returned to itself, and she stood at the beginning and the end.

Alberga, working in the gardens, saw a phantasm. She was pulling turnips, great heavy clots of vegetation. She dropped the one she heaved up on to its foot and it passed right through. Alberga squinted. Her weak eyes saw only a blur. She spoke and it vanished. Like smoke it seemed to her, and so sudden that she doubted what she had seen. It must have been the late sun dazzling from the monastery roof, that and too much fasting made her eyes deceive her.

Scolastica had been in a dead faint, as she sometimes was. At these times they could not rouse her. For days she would remain like this. Then they would hear her yelping like a pup as the thing re-entered her body. Werberga tried to administer whatever help she could, pouring infusions into the cup that hung near the bars. But Scolastica was dying this time, she had been out of her body for too long and was weak, too weak to lift the cup and drink. Her arms were no thicker than kindling. She had made her body hollow, she could not animate it any more than her phantasm could be made to run. Yet she watched life around her with eyes and reason that were clear enough. Her mind leaped away from her body's feeble state. She understood that she was between life and death, neither in this world nor ready for the next.

She preached the separation of mind and body. And she put it to practice. If she stayed away too long the dull pieces of matter would not re-absorb her spirit. She was not fond of the body, yet she constantly returned to it because through it she could pass on her knowledge.

'If the body of Christ is in everyone, then through Christ it is transformed. Like Christ risen from the dead, the body of Christ is everywhere, in all places at the same time.'

The sisters listened to her as she instructed that the body was a temporary resting place, the spirit prisoned within. To free the soul consciously meant that the body would suffer on account of being bound to the other.

'What do we care for our bodies? What of them? Let the spirit loose! Let it be free and in our deaths we will taste such freedom as we have never known! I have glimpsed it.'

After such sermons she would become as one dead and not move for days, until the order began to grow concerned thinking that it must be time. Always as the decision was taken to exhume what they took to be her corpse from the cell, the chest would suddenly heave, as air filled up her flattened lungs. Breathing, so shallow as to be imperceptible at first, would become steadily more noticeable. Movement in her chest was enough to dispel fears of her death and eventually she would move again, confused at first, as one coming out of a heavy sleep. But it was not sleep she returned from, for during those times when her body lay still and death-like, the nuns saw her in the garden, then in the scriptorium, always motionless.

'It is possible to animate these phantasms,' she instructed. 'But the effort is beyond human strength. Taking on appearance saps everything. Only by extra-human strength, and God's grace, can a phantasm be like one of us. Just as the Archangel descended to Mary, he spoke and moved and appeared solid to tell the Blessed Virgin that she would bear the Son of God, while he was eternally present in glory in the kingdom of Heaven. He was in two places. His phantasm walked on earth.'

But the nuns were disturbed. It troubled them when they felt her come upon them, when they saw the dim shape that was Scolastica, so silent, so unworldly that they thought they were being judged. And it must be great evil or great good which caused such things to pass. They could be misled, and the convent in the grip of a demonic force. Such were their doubts.

'Bylocation could be studied as a branch of humanism, although the nominalists will disagree with me, but it is a matter of basic transference from one substance to another just as the bread becomes body, or organic matter decays and so changes. For what is this decay but new life? Out of putrefaction grows the first shoot.'

In the mill house, the small, circular, flagstoned room with shelves of bluish slate, the sacks of wheat and barley waited to be ground. Around the walls, winnowing trays and baskets hung on nails. Sister Martha the miller took a handful of seeds and dropped them through the hole in the smaller top stone. She turned the wooden wheel and the stones began to revolve, round and round until the seed had split. Then Sister Martha lowered the top stone and began to turn again.

She sang deafly as she turned the wheel, but not for long, this was to be the coarse flour for baking the heavy black bread that they ate every day. It was repetitive and monotonous, and she was free to dwell on God usually, but she could not. She felt troubled.

Although she did not hear much she often saw further. She understood the unconscious gestures of the sisters in her silent world. To her, silence was a gift and not much of a tribulation in a life devoted to contemplation, and given to sparing use of speech. With her way of hearing the unspoken, she read faces for the things they could not utter and so heard more than those who relied on words alone.

She knew that many of the nuns were greatly troubled by the sightings of the old infirmarian. In their hearts some felt that it was not the work of God but of the Unspeakable One. As she thought it, a chill passed over her. A shadow fell across her then vanished, a cloud blocked out the sun.

All day the clouds had been moving, they raced each other in the sky and assumed strange shapes. Martha watched hunchbacked men and dogs running in a pack, the face of a church official, hook-nosed and warty like the last bishop that had come to sniff around them. But he had discovered nothing. And she had been extra deaf that day repeating all his questions and not able to lip-read from his mouth. She laughed to herself.

'It will take more than a bishop or his man the abbot to frighten me . . .'

She looked up knowing she was watched. The old infirmarian stood over her. Her silent rival who could do nothing to prevent her deafness despite all her sciences and learning. As postulants they had both tried to be the most self-effacing. Martha's deafness had won the battle between them easily.

Scolastica hovered. Her feet did not touch the ground. Sharp blades of grass shot through them. Clouds passed through the old nun's face, obliterating her features. Martha squinted, no longer certain of what she saw. Scolastica seemed to fade then return, more solid this time.

'Think to disturb me, do you? What trick is this you work on us? Better to be able to work and pray in one place. What's the use of this play-acting?' she shouted deafly. 'Better to be in one's body and make it work than be half a soul cast drifting. All this hopeless travelling and coming forth. You don't work as I do.'

Saying this she picked up a handful of grains, tossed it towards the shape which instantly vanished. She laughed toothlessly.

'That's shown you. Blown away like chaff!' she cackled.

Outside two nuns were winnowing, throwing the grain up into the air to land upon a soft white linen square. They watched as the stalk and waste blew away and the heavier grain dropped on to the pile.

They heard Sister Martha talking inside the mill house.

'What use? What use?' they heard her shout, and they put their heads round the door to see her bent over her fat stomach, laughing.

The light stuff blew away to land further off. What had happened to start the old nun off so loudly? Whatever had come to pass in the convent could no longer be hidden, for even their deafest member now heard tell of it.

When Sister Gertrude went to inspect the skeps she became so disturbed that she took to burning sulphur underneath, destroying the swarm, lest they flew up and stung her. She was sure that someone watched her all the time.

It was the uncertainty. If only they could be assured that it was the work of Heaven and not Hell, they would be able to resume their tasks in peace, but each sister in turn became agitated. All over the convent things went badly. The lay sisters could not settle to their labours and prayers were disturbed by anxieties. At common mass the nuns were scared that Scolastica might appear on the monks' side and their voices were tremulous and quavery as they let the male voices dominate the plainsong. In the dairy they paddled the milk so fast that the cream was spoilt and would not separate. The cheeses they had hung just two weeks back turned mouldy, and this they thought was a sign that they were out of favour.

14

BUILDING

THE ABBESS SAW THE convent from a distance, the square bell-tower of the monks' side rising on higher ground. She would be in full view as she crossed the surrounding fields, but that was the way she must walk. She would go through the large gates to receive the abbot's blessing on her safe return. She had to re-enter Fortitude proudly, not in fear and shame.

And on the nuns' side there were many who did not know her at first. Werberga, although her relief was great, was hesitant to come forward. There was a silence rather than a welcome as they watched her.

The abbess was thinner, as if her body had been worn away by rough contact with the outside world. It had been an abrasive time for her, causing her face to become lined.

She appeared to be looking for something. She scrutinised their faces as if she wanted extra details that were lost to her. Altered, she returned with something they called greater wisdom, but the older sisters knew she had suffered to acquire it.

Where once she turned a questioning face, always willing to learn, now she seemed perplexed and tired. She did not talk much in those first few days, but remained in her cell. They thought she was secretive. The world was a place of confusion and she had not been able to leave it outside. This time she brought the journey back with her. Aelreda had the memory of her actions and her secret.

The sisters did not know the small mewling thing that was handed over from its wet-nurse, passed inside the turn-gate where its screams could be heard. On the other side the abbess waited and held the tiny infant once, then handed it over to Sister Gertrude who was responsible for the convent children.

'Lucky you chanced by and heard it Mother Abbess. The poor creature's frozen. May God have mercy on the mother's soul.'

Aelreda would have no more contact with the baby and she watched as the warm squealing thing, bright as a sucking-pig, was lifted away. Yet she felt relief. It was done. Now her life could continue, and with that thought some of her vigour returned.

So the child of the convent came to be among the order. The child was weaned roughly and rudely. Shrieking, it learned its first lesson: that no one would comfort it, as no one came to nurse it. The light grey eyes watched the ceiling listlessly, until finding its thumb the child sucked away to escaping sleep, a state it would crave all its further days, to pass away from the life which luck's hand had dealt.

An accident gave it life, let it breathe, and it sensed its non-existence, for it was the by-product of Fortune, that goddess who stared down once and for the rest of the child's life turned away and would not stop the wheel.

Aelreda sent a message to Mother Albergisten with a traveller who followed a pilgrim's route. A careful letter returned within the month. It was fastened with many seals and folded cleverly so that it might not be opened by mistake. An extra precaution of wax smeared along the folds prevented anyone tampering with it. The abbot handed it to her through the communion grille and sounded grave as he expressed hopes that it was not another instruction for her to leave the convent, with her so recently returned to them.

Equally the nuns were disturbed, and Werberga, dreading a second stint as acting head watched Aelreda carefully as she opened the single page out, flattening the folds with her left hand. They wondered what caused the parent house to break its long silence, when throughout all of their beloved abbess's time away from them, they received no word of information or reassurance. Throughout that time there had been not a hint of news.

The abbess understood Mother Albergisten's predicament. How could the head nun of the convent lie to her sisters, for what else could she do to maintain the secrecy of the second delegation? Her only method was to keep silence, a long silence which she could in part now break.

The letter first rejoiced in the safe return of Aelreda to her convent, but in the following neat lines mentioned that there was cause to lament. Their prayers were requested for the souls of five of their sisters. Aelreda understood what the supreme head of the order meant by this message. Out of the delegation, apart from herself, two sisters had made it back safely. Only two of those brave, stout-hearted women. And she understood that the quest for a relic had failed completely. Tears pricked her eyes.

But the next lines were joyful. In a southern house a nun was reported to have had visions. Divine messages were uttered by her. And these incidents had been regular enough for the local churchmen to begin an investigation to see if the power that moved their sister was from Heaven, or was diabolic.

Mother Albergisten urged them all to pray. If a sister in their order was found to be in the presence of the holy spirit, none might dispute her authority. They would be able to state their case through a divine mouthpiece so they could choose to stay aloof from the larger monastic groups and develop the rule to suit their own needs.

Such a holy woman among them would give them extra worthiness. Aelreda knew that they must be above rebuke while the investigation took place. She felt anxious for the nun. Female mystics were more feared than men, because women were easier for the Devil to seduce. She knew that too well. All the order must pray that the examination be tolerable, that their dear sister have the strength to endure whatever was necessary to disclose the spirit's nature.

The letter ended with good news; already the stigmata after bathing had been seen to continue to bleed.

The nuns of Fortitude were excited when their abbess read out the message. None more so than Werberga, who was gladdened at her script without the extra responsibility for the convent. Although she had struggled to fulfil the role in her superior's absence, it had been a great strain and she knew that the business at Fortitude was not as it ought to be.

When she spoke to Aelreda about Scolastica, the abbess exclaimed that one holy woman was enough for any order. It was plain that she was frightened by the developments.

'How vocal has she become?' she asked the scribe, who did her best to tell of everything that had happened in her absence.

'But we are to be beyond reproach ... if any news of this reaches the outside ...'

Aelreda had come home to Fortitude wanting a refuge, somewhere she could hide and be safe from the world. There must be no tales, no rumours, especially now with the promise of future worthiness for the order. There was to be no loose, babbling talk that might ripple beyond the building, bringing the investigators down upon them.

'The position of the cell is a mistake. It is too close to the monks' side. I would never have allowed it.'

Werberga looked at her feet.

'What can we do when she begins to teach? How can we silence her when everything she utters might be heard on the other side of the grille? Did you not think of this?'

'But Mother, she was so persuasive. I had not the skill to argue with her. I could not deflect her from this once her mind was fixed. All I could do was to follow her orders.'

Aelreda could not blame the scribe when she had been no match for the one time infirmarian either.

'The expense is worrying. It is so costly, and so wasteful. All around I see evidence of hurried work, piles of rubble . . .'

'No, Mother,' Werberga interrupted. 'Some of it is good stone . . .'

'And what might we do with it?' Aelreda asked, raising an eyebrow.

Werberga looked away.

Already groups of women waited outside the gate at Fortitude. They came for instruction, but were denied entry by a nervous gate-keeper.

'Let them stand outside. Scolastica must not have disciples. The cell has prevented her hands from working, somehow we must stop her tongue.'

Werberga was glad that it was not her decision. The convent might continue as it used to, when to her each day was clear and tidy in its aims. Scolastica was a problem she would no longer be expected to solve. Despite her abbess's disapproval she rushed to chapel to give thanks. She felt lighter in her heart than she had for many months and she longed to settle at her work without distraction. She prayed gladly, knowing that before the day was out she would be in her place in the scriptorium. Already she was planning the next group of borders she would draw for the collection of prayers.

It was late when Aelreda crept out to the anchorite's cell and stood listening. There was no sound from within, yet Werberga had spoken with fright of the words Scolastica screamed and of the women who would make the gate-keeper busy given a chance.

Should she speak with her? Something made her feel that more words would be troublesome. She understood the old nun well enough to know that her silence could not be guaranteed. But the order had to survive. Any false reports now might ruin them. She herself had placed them all at risk by sending for the child to be entered secretly among them.

In her hand she grasped a black stone she had carried back from the Sisters of Compassionate Darkness. It had healing properties. Deftly she slipped it between the bars and heard it thud onto the soft earth of the cell floor before she hurried away silently. Without seeing the old nun, she had made her decision.

In the half-light of evening, Scolastica turned toward the sound and felt about on all fours until her hand found something. Spherical and smooth she held it in her palm, not realising that her remaining time for feeling, touching and having bodily sensations was rapidly coming to a close.

Time continued to run out as sand or water does to mark the days passing. Outside her cell changes were being made in rotas and duties, but such things no longer affected her.

Scolastica often shouted loudly for days on end. Then she would become quiet. No one knew how long either might last. Some times they thought she was dead.

The nuns and lay sisters were woken one night by the sound of the rattle being swung in the cloisters. They rose and knocked on doors to rouse each other as they went as quickly as they could to chapel. Who was dying that the call to prayer came so suddenly? In the choir stalls they looked around to see who was missing. Their abbess was not amongst them, and several of the lay sisters began to fret, but Gertrude, who had woken deaf Martha by boxing her ears, put them at their ease.

'I called for our abbess on the way down from the dorter, but the door was open and she had left her cell.'

'Then she must be the one who called with the rattle.'

It was dark in the chapel except for the flickering altar light left burning and the shafts of moonlight through the narrow windows. The crucifix gleamed, catching the light of the tapers some of the sisters carried. The gold reflected in their faces as they knelt.

Aelreda followed in last. She was perspiring. The rattle was heavy and she had raced from the cloisters with it.

'My beloved sisters,' she said, turning to face them. The

order waited for what she had to say, their faces illuminated by tallow, their dark eyes widening.

'Sisters, our beloved sister Scolastica is finally at peace. Help us to accept our duty. We are tonight to send her in glory.'

In the silence that followed Aelreda whispered to the cell wall. 'Give us your blessing Sister.'

From the anchorite's cell there was no movement. Scolastica slept. Aelreda peered inside the bars and saw the old nun, barely human in aspect, coiled upon the floor. Turning to the assembly of nuns she spoke authoritatively.

'It is important that we bury our dear sister before the sun rises. Locked inside her cell that none might enter. It is not fitting that we should see her in undignified death. To stare on her cold death without hands to clean and prepare her mortal remains would be a violation of our sister's passing from us. Let her be dignified in death. In cover of the night we might not look upon our beloved sister's shell, but working together to seal her tomb, we will remember how she was in life.'

In the choir nuns moved their heads in agreement, and quickly the lay sisters placed candles at intervals to form a procession. They would make a swift ceremony in shallow night.

Werberga wondered if this meant that Scolastica's truths were at last being affirmed. Maybe after death someone would put forward her name for the examination. She might become the next saint, the patron of women everywhere, and the order would be renowned.

Nuns were weeping. In the dark, shapes ran, darted with great haste, and the chapel was full of whispering. Wheels clattered upon the tiles. Turning, some saw Aelreda pull a narrow cart into the porch. The stronger lay workers among them rushed to take it from her. It was stacked with left-over white stone and they wheeled it right down until it was almost on the altar.

Now they understood; the abbess lifted out a small slab

and began to position this in place across the only opening of the cell. Together they could construct a fine edifice for Scolastica's tomb.

'At last, at last!' Werberga thought. Scolastica's work might now be recognised. She was truly blessed.

'This cell will be a shrine,' Werberga said. 'Long after we are gone, after the stones have turned to dust, her name will be remembered . . .'

'A shrine, Sister, yes a shrine, we will always pray for her,' Aelreda whispered. 'She will be rewarded in Heaven.'

'She will save the order.'

But the abbess said nothing.

The sisters worked past their exhaustion until, like the procession of the damned, they knew nothing else but the torturous work in front of them. The repetition of the task of lifting stones seemed eternal, and each one pondered her own death.

The tiny cell extended up as a hollow tower, the stones circling round. Some bars were still visible as the pieces were moved closer, to seal the gap. While just a slit remained, something seemed to break off, it bounced and skidded on the chapel floor. The nuns stopped in their labours and strained to hear.

'It is a chip of stone, that is all,' Aelreda told them. But she knew it was the piece of black stone thrown from inside the cell. She would return in daylight to find it.

Inside the cell, Scolastica listened to noises. Outside she heard weeping, the sound of something heavy dragging along the stone floor, the sharp sounds of chipping and hammering. She knew that they were working on her cell. A ladder was straddled across her bars and she watched in the grey gloom as the sisters worked themselves into a frenzy, passing up regular shaped stones. They worked ceaselessly into the dawn, constructing something on the top of her tiny cell, extending it upwards, towards God.

It was to be her last glimpse of the world before the darkness in which she found herself.

Eventually the last stone caught in the wall and the sisters smeared red clay around the opening and scraped off the surplus as the stone sank into the space.

The round column stood, newly appointed at the foot of the altar, like a miniature tower. It was slightly taller than a giant of a man might be and slender, giving it the illusion of height. A strange thing to have, an enclosed monument and burial place for the remains of Scolastica. Some could hear the sounds of mice scratching. Outside the chapel, birds ruffled their feathers and began bright, happy songs welcoming the sun. Keen-eyed they picked up the outlines of the day as it emerged from the night and they whistled into the faded morning.

It was after this that Oda, the librarian, crept back to the outhouses. Now it was necessary to ask permission from the abbess before going there, a new rule which she brought in on her return. The librarian hoped that no one saw her as she trod towards the building. She knew that within the following days a new infirmarian would be chosen, so she had to hurry while the place was still empty.

The heavy door was not locked, and swung back easily without sound. She could not light a candle for fear of being seen, but she made out the black outline of the wooden chest. Her heart was pounding. Paper rustled under her feet as she trod; debris was strewn about, for no attempt would be made to sort through or clean up the area until the new infirmarian was elected.

No one had been out there since she discovered the two postulants. From what she could see, everything was as she remembered it. She prayed it was. As she lifted the lid an outline of a book appeared. Gratefully she seized it and without waiting slipped out of the door. Quickly, she returned across the yard. Every time she saw a sister she shuddered. She almost dropped the volume when deaf Martha came upon her suddenly from behind.

'Did I scare you?' the old nun asked her loudly. Oda could only nod. Why should Sister Martha think anything was untoward? It was her reaction alone which might give a clue. Her face felt damp.

'You are nervous. We are all listening to shadows still. But they've gone, they've gone. Back to the Devil . . . back to the Devil where they should have remained. Their souls are at rest now . . .' the deaf nun continued to walk, '. . . and there are no more phantasms. I haven't seen her for a while. She doesn't visit me anymore.' She shook her head. 'I expect it's for the best.'

The librarian tightened her grip on the book as Sister Martha passed. It was heavy and she dreaded dropping it. Werberga's trained eyes would soon spot any tell-tale marks along the binding. On the flight of steps to the library she stopped and looked around the yard. She did not want anyone to see her enter this way. No one would think it odd of her, it was her duty to bring books across to the refectory or to the chapter house. Yet her heart thumped with fear.

She unlocked the door. The library was a dark, narrow place with light coming from the high openings in the walls during the day. But nothing lit it now. All the tapers were out and she did not light one but went cautiously in the dark having double bolted the door behind her. As her eyes became accustomed she could see the one free chain hanging loosely from the beam along the wall where the volumes were chained. Quickly she returned the book to it and felt, as the lock turned, that it was greatly weakened for being forced. The metal prongs quivered into place.

She was proud of her library. Since the abbess returned Werberga was able to resume her duties as chief scribe. Her eagerness was an inspiration to them all. They needed to feel that they were again involved in God's work with a passion that would let them pass away from the troubled past. The abbess had ambitions to build up a fine library of a dozen or more new works. But Oda shook her head when she looked at the one she carried. To copy it and decorate it fittingly would be the work of a lifetime. Already Werberga had started training the younger sisters as copyists. She set them pages to ink each day, and they sat heartlessly in the cloisters, tracing words and outlines which the following day they wrote on top of until it was impossible to read. Now, they had a steady supply of old parchment to be faded and re-used. The student inkers erased their previous work, and scratched out lines of copy. Now whenever Oda passed by she was greeted by bowed heads and the scratching of pens. Never had there been such a concentration upon work. Their abbess spoke of making a larger scriptorium to accommodate the inkers. But she felt uncomfortable about it. Books were borne out of years of study, not one after the other without thought.

She was given the task of ensuring that nothing which might smack of heresy should be on display in the library. The abbess wanted to put most of Scolastica's work to the fire before the rest of the convent knew of its existence. As librarian she was relieved when Werberga requested the pages be re-used like all others, if only to give her students parchment to practise on, instead of waxed blocks like the boy scholars from town. And the abbess warned them that the order must be beyond reproach. No one was to produce another work across Scolastica's text, in case the old writing was ever discovered. On this provision Scolastica's medical tracts were faded from the remaining pages under the watchful eyes of the senior nuns.

Heretical as some of the work might be, and none of that had been proven, there was a move to secrecy within the order. The abbess seemed to be constantly watching her back as if some terrible dream trod upon her days. She was so nervous that the senior nuns, believing she knew of a great threat to them, could only agree that all which was dangerous or which might threaten their existence be removed before anyone outside got to hear of it.

The librarian loved books; so much knowledge condensed

and handed down to be kept for ever. She could not bring herself to destroy everything.

She stroked the spine of the book she held. It was crude. They had not the resources to train a bookbinder so they sent work through to the men's side where such a skilled worker was to be found. The pages of parchment would come back to them, sewn into a neat package, without seams showing, and the leather work finely stitched.

But this torn book was entirely their own, its cover rough and the spine lumpy. It was split from the poorest hide and looked pickled rather than tanned. She had heard that in times of famine books were seized by ravenous mobs who boiled the leather to eat. Maybe it was fortunate that they did not house many magnificently bound works.

The abbess wanted them to create a book in part payment of their debt. They had no white stone left to return, so must cover the full amount. Such a work would have to have costly binding and lettering such as only Werberga could at this stage make. Unless they developed some good inkers their debt would be held for a long time.

Her fingers played up and down the crude leather back. She leaned it across the wooden pole and started to read, but the light had faded so rapidly that she could only see a few illustrations. But she knew what was in it and would read more of it before it was stripped of its message, the pages restretched to await the shaky lines of uncertain Latin which would be scratched upon its greyed surface.

In this book were drawings; stages of a woman's condition, the baby coiled inside as if the skin of the belly was transparent. Inside the guts of woman sleeps a tiny man. Miniature head, ears and feet. Above this hovers a disc, the soul. She stared hard at these pages wanting to remember. The small man swelled and grew and as it did, so the disc enlarged, still hovering over the female form. Then the soul descended. Scolastica had shown it passing over the woman's head to follow a path until it reached the babe, where it remained like a shell surrounding an egg.

There were columns with notations and figures; different lengths of time, from inception to birth. For a female child the soul took longer to cover the baby. Then it was seen descending when the female baby was so large that it appeared to fill up all the empty sack space inside the woman.

Throughout most of its growth the miniature woman was soulless. This was as Scolastica taught. This was what she meant by the removal of base matter. And there were calculations to determine the gender of such matter, to detect the presence or absence of spirit, of higher life which would keep the growing life intact.

Oda wanted to commit these things to memory before she let the book be taken. Is this what the abbess was so frightened of when she spoke about the need for silence? Was this teaching against God?

There was much confusion at this time, and she prayed that the dark days would end. Even with her, there were sisters who fell silent whenever she passed. The convent was given over to whisperings, to half heard rumours, wild beyond imagination. Even Werberga had agreed to the removal of anything heretical from the library and was nervous for her own works. Once so great a follower of Scolastica, she had changed through fear, and she was troubled because she held herself responsible for the debt they had incurred.

Recently Werberga as head scribe called at the library and tore pages from the book that was still chained, insisting that they had to be faded. The librarian clutched the remains after she left and decided to keep her counsel.

She removed a metal strap from another volume and chained this about the secret book. The strap was rusty and creaked as she pulled it around the binding. It took three attempts before the padlock bit. One key she would keep about her waist cord, but she would pretend to have mislaid the other until she had the work fixed in her memory. Then she would present the book to Werberga in all humility, to be sliced into loose sheets and left soaking in the lime pit to fade out the dangerous words.

Werberga dipped her pen into the well and slowly traced across the page.

The scriptorium was empty. She had to commit what she had seen to parchment, but she hesitated. She had taken a sheet from the lime pit and stretched it several days in advance, brooding over her task. She began nervously. Better to write it as a riddle.

Her hand quivered. It was her duty to record all. For honour she must salve her conscience. Slowly she began to fill in the letters, not carefully, but in a rough manner. In some lines the large square capitals seemed at odds with the smaller ones which remained in place from a previous text.

She did not know where the page came from. Strange to think it might be one of Scolastica's own. And whose was that version of neat, sloping script, faded to softest grey?

She could not compose the first line and she thought of words to tell the deed. Then her hand began to draw instead as she pictured it. Along the margin she made a tower with a tiny barred window. On top of this a sword, for had not Scolastica been a martyr for the order's continuance? She suspected as much. Scolastica had not died, but was suffocated by mistake. Only Aelreda pronounced her dead.

She took another brush and filled up the sword with kermes extract. Let it survive like a stain, it might show through each successive layer of script. She made another outline, a narrow hand drawn in spiders' lines as fine as bone, brittle with starvation. The hand protruded from the bars, clawed in the air with curling nails. But Werberga could not let it stay. With black ink she washed it over, sent it back into darkness.

The Convent of Fortitude. The Year of Our Lord 906.

Overnight it arose. Where there had been nothing now there is.
And with it, weariness beset the convent.
Such dullness settled with the dust of masonry as it fell equally on

all things, none escaped, even the beasts in the outhouses. Coughing
and swallowing we went about our daily work with poor spirits
while our bodies were covered in the grey dust of the dead.

Our brothers in God marvelled at the work. The speed and
certainty which had created it rather than the intricacy of its
structure.

The cell was complete. Such amounts of quarried white stone
being left to us.

It being greatly expensive we have sent a book in part payment
to the abbot, for he furnished us with the means to obtain the stone.
But it is a debt of many years.

It stands, a wretched edifice keeping an odious truth. I can
no longer write these things for in this place pages are set to the
candle.

Quickly Werberga powderd the sheet, then rolled it up. If it
blotted there was little she could do. There was no time. She
hid the roll inside her tunic sleeve. She would keep it about
her person till her death. Only the corpse washer would take
it from her. She crept out softly to join her sisters in the chapel
where she could not look at the new stonework, a mock tower
without entrance or exit, but she felt it cover her in its dark self
no less.

PART FOUR

SCRATCHES ON THE SURFACE

15

DREAMING

Siobhan got into a rhythmic swing labelling and sticking the white gummed squares on the fly leaves. First she removed worn labels. She read names of girls who went ahead of her. Some she could put faces to, others were forgotten, as if they never existed. There were labels dating back to the 1940's; these books had been over twenty years in use. Mostly Shakespeare and the big volumes on art history, and logarithm tables. She expected that the Latin primers too had not been revised.

She worked steadily with her hands occupied. The repetition of the work lulled her, calmed her. She let herself drift, seeing over and over the scene where some young man stumbled upon her, always meeting by chance. And he was always faceless. She could only get as far as to whether his hair was dark or ginger, straight or curly, and the scene would evaporate. She never got to picture his face. But handsome, that was taken for granted.

Walking down the street with him later, everyone else in her dream would stare at him. The girls at school would be jealous – or admiring. That was better. They would admire him.

But that was not the way it happened. She waited for her quiet, careful inventions, but the only ones she met were at a disco. There was no chance about it. Then there would be the frenzied necking and an embarrassed silence after as mouths once so intimate became strangers again, with words more personal than touch.

Last Saturday night had been the same as every other. She spent all week looking forward to it, but when it came what was it?

The bouncers always looked her up and down. Torn between feeling that she would give them no trouble and knowing that she was under-age. She was seventeen and looked it. Shirley could pass for twenty.

'She's too old in the head by far,' her father would say about her friend. 'God knows where you'll end up with the likes of her.'

But her mother always supported her. She wanted to push her daughter into adulthood, and if going out on a Saturday night was a first step, she would not stop her. Grow up, get a job, bring home some money, that was what being an adult meant.

The faceless romantic hero pushed past her mother.

'She's with me, ma'am,' his soft accent drawled.

He stood tall in his uniform. The United States Airforce. Maybe the Navy. He put his pack of Camels back inside the breast pocket of his flying jacket. Oh, definitely airforce. A notebook, a pass – not cigarettes, no. Not a smoker.

'I'll make sure she's home on time ma'am.'

That was the problem with fantasy men. They disappeared when you needed them. Last Saturday she could have done with his help.

Shirley stood in front of the mirror in the ladies.

'We look a couple of gawps in this light.' She back combed her thin hair. Under the strip lights they both looked sick.

'Have I got a turn in my eye when I go sideways?' Shirley rolled her eyes around. 'Only I had my photo taken in one of those booths in the chemist. In the bottom one I'm as cross-eyed as they come.'

'You're all right.' Siobhan pulled out her new glitter eye shadow.

'That's great,' Shirley said and with sweeping strokes she put some on top of the purple she already wore.

The mirror was tarnished and the floor damp with urine and bits of soggy kleenex. Shirley's eyes were drawn in carefully. She wore make up whenever she could. At school it was forbidden, but she would put mascara on before leaving the grounds. All weekend she hid beneath a solid mask of pancake and the deep black lines she drew around her eyes. She spent time on these, they would stay in place all weekend. She washed around them until Monday.

Last summer Shirley went on holiday to a coastal resort and for two weeks would not go into the sea. It would wash away her eyes, those silver fish scales which glittered every Saturday night as she blinked under the flashing lights.

The music was loud. After a while they adjusted. It seeped into Siobhan, her body moved to it.

'Breaking down the walls of heartache, I've been breaking down the walls of heartache . . .'

Suddenly someone was dancing with her.

'Name?' he said.

He breathed through his mouth. He was the friend of whoever was with Shirley, the one with a beard. But hers had pimples. She always got the friend.

She stuck another label into the front of a book and re-arranged the features of her dance partner.

'I'm just in town for a few days . . . maybe you could show a stranger around?'

A tall man with a four day beard. She dug her boots into the dust of Main Street as he led his horse gently to a post to tether it. The horse nuzzled him. He turned back and watched her.

'Do you know the sheriff in these parts?' he asked.

They sat down together, all four. Always four. Within a few minutes the beard had his hand down Shirley's cardigan.

'They seem to be getting on well,' his friend said.

Siobhan told him she was learning karate and was thinking of entering a convent.

'What did you do that for?' Shirley asked her in the ladies. 'He was all right.'

She stood up and carried a pile of completed books over to the cupboard. There was another stack to be got through which she had not noticed. She transferred all the labelled books over and stood them on the floor in neat rows. Then she began on the next stack. Life had to have meaning. She could cook, shop and fight. That was her mother's existence. That and the odd word exchanged with a shop assistant. The fishmonger last week told Siobhan to get right to the top.

'You and the mackerel can do it!' he said and winked. 'Fish is wonderful for the brains.'

Her mother muttered about being in a hurry.

'Idiot!' she said as soon as they were out on the street. But sometimes her mother told everything to the fishmonger, to anyone who'd listen. Siobhan hated that. Sometimes, walking down the high street she felt everyone knew what was going through her mind. Yesterday the breadman shook his head, tutting as she took the loaves from him.

'I thought you were a good girl Siobhan Doolin,' he said. 'You've your mammy's heart broken.'

And for what? Her mother did not know what to tell people. Staying on at school was the euphemism.

'Get right to the top,' the fishmonger said, and her mother dragged her out of the shop.

Siobhan wondered what you missed by being in a convent. She thought hard. Shirley told her that boys made her go weak. Kissing them turned her knees to water, her legs dissolved. Any boy.

'Jesus, do you think I'm going to be one of those nymphomaniacs?' she asked her. 'Only I've heard that it's a medical disorder.'

Secretly Siobhan dreaded that whatever Shirley was she

was its opposite. Numb like the gutted fishes she carried home in newspaper.

'I trust the fish,' the man said, giving her a wink and a wrapped paper parcel.

Siobhan put a hand up to catch back her hair, and it smelt of fish.

As she worked at the labelling she felt a dizzy whirring sensation. It seemed to be inside her ears. Like when her father hit her, then she would hear the sound of air, the slapping of fists. Her father's hands were large, squat as a boxer's, primed by punching.

She slapped white squares onto pages feeling angry. Thudding.

Bone onto skin. Lousy, lousy skin with all its pain.

She counted the books and checked them, ticked the list of ones she had re-labelled and began tearing out from a new pile.

She dreamed about the lapping of water, of wave upon wave as monks set sail. In the scratch of paper she heard boats crash upon rocks. In the turn of a page she heard her father ripping up the gilt-edged programme. He swore the school was a terrible place, full of toffs and snobs and God didn't know what.

That was last term. He'd had a fight on the bus coming back from the prize ceremony.

A drunk carrying an accordion had over-balanced and sat on her mother. The bus was packed. People were crushed up against each other and the drunken man was hanging from a leather strap. No one offered him a seat. People looked away.

Her mother was facing him on the side seats. His knees touched hers. The bus turned a corner, he fell forward. The accordion sprang open, a horrible musical vomit, fanning out wide. The man struggled but could not balance. Her father ordered him to stand up, but the drunk could not manage to. Her mother was crushed underneath and frightened.

A man in an overcoat, although it was a warm evening, said the man was drunk.

'There is no use shouting at him,' he said calmly and offered the drunken man a hand, leaning in front of her father who swung out and laid one on the overcoat and the overcoat let drop the drunk who stumbled to avoid her mother, but sat on her again.

'Just who do you think you are?'

Her father was rigid with indignity. Being shown up on a bus full of people.

Now the drunk was up on unsteady feet, wavering between them, the accordion ranging in and out to accompany his movements.

The conductor rang the funny business signal, three short strokes on the bell. The bus pulled up smartly and the driver came round to see what was happening.

The conductor put the drunk and her father off together. Siobhan watched her father on the pavement, he looked confused and stared in disbelief at the man in uniform, his mouth opening like a stupid fish. Then her mother started crying.

'It's a shame, a shame,' someone said and the conductor let him get back on.

'But no carrying on,' he warned him. 'You can stand on the platform.'

Siobhan looked the other way.

When they got home he took the programme out of his pocket and ripped up the details of her exam success. The cause of all the trouble. Her souvenir lay in shreds.

'Next time I'll make a real effort and fail the lot!' she said. So he hit her across the face. The perfect end to a perfect day.

'What do you do at school?' the boy asked her at the dance.

'Karate,' she told him.

But it was her father who urged her to go on. To stay at school and be educated. All the time her mother wanted her to work in British Home Stores.

'They're got staff canteens and pensions.'

She listened to the sound of paper ripping as she tore off label after label. 1940, 1945. Who needs souvenirs? She wanted no memory of life. She wanted to enter a new world and shake off all her past. Be reborn in Christ. A new soul and a new spirit. God would dissolve those things she could no longer stand, the noise, the yelling, the foul tempers and the ache in her ears, each time her father forgot himself.

Was there room for all their souls in Heaven? Her father prayed for forgiveness each time. She imagined him being turned away and saw herself praying for him to be admitted, not out of any kindness, but with a sense of her own power.

When the ocean was still unmapped, Saint Columba floated away from the land, without any promise of safety, to build new monasteries. Stone upon stone, cross formation.

Siobhan listened. Around her now the noise of building. She heard them work. Her father's fists beat into successive layers, built up the edifice of her resistance. Her hatred grew until it was all around, suffocating. Fragments of pain one upon the other, stone upon stone.

Inside it must be totally dark. A dark which eyes cannot become used to. Nothing to see, not even a bat or cat or some nocturnal animal can see in this. This is not the dark of night. This is the sightlessness of nothing. A bat might fly out of control through it. There is no air. It is hot and suffocating. The anchorite stood still.

It is hot, dark and terrible.

This is death. Airless, sightless, without movement.

Did the anchorite put out her arm, touch the wall in front? If she were to stretch she might feel with her other hand the wall behind her back. Not quite an arm's span. With elbows bent she turns in a slow circle touching the inside walls of the tower as no one else will. Only she knows this tower now. She knows every brick and the raw new patch like a graze. Her calloused finger tips, rough from tracing its surface, have become her eyes. They describe the tower. They offer, through the many dents and grooves, familiar reassurance of the end. Something falls, hits her forehead; an insect, a beetle by its weight, plummets to its death. She screams, but it is soundless. Soon it will be her turn to fall. What is at her feet? Is this state her eternal punishment, to pray for death and be denied? The walls sweat. She listens to those who wait outside, for the last sounds of scratching.

Siobhan heard noises on the stairway. Sister Cecile came back into the store room.

'Haven't you finished yet?' she asked, seeing the girl gazing into space.

Under the girl's eyes, dark shadows, and a bruise, yellowing now over her face. What had the girl seen? Cecile could not imagine. But it was violent no doubt, and she knew that she must do something.

The girl's eyes had grown as black as the ink in the tower and as fathomless. Cecile recognised the look. It was anything but vacant. A stare that was steeped in unhappiness, as secret as the dark. She had to know what Siobhan had seen.

The girl slowly turned her head, and seemed surprised to see the nun.

'Sister?' she asked, not sure if she had been asked a question.

'I don't want anything,' Cecile said. 'Why don't you leave these now and finish them another time. You've done a lot.'

The girl surveyed the pile of books and looked bewildered as if she saw them for the first time. Then she nodded. Wordlessly she left the store room.

Cecile leaned on a chairback. The time had come to speak to the girl's parents.

16

PUZZLING

CECILE TOOK OUT THE parchment and carefully spread it on the desk. It was a long twisted strip of paper. She was scared in case it disintegrated, but she saw faint markings through it and suspected that there was writing on its inside. Her breath was shallow, she was terrified of destroying the piece by clumsy gestures. She stopped. Really, she should take it to Alan Wainsworth or the older man, tell them what she had found and ask one of them to unfold it. But even as she hesitated she knew that she would have to open it flat, now that she had started. Her curiosity was unbearable. She could not wait with it half unfurled until they were in the school. And she wanted to see it, wanted to be the first to witness its message after centuries of hiding.

Where it had been folded and re-folded the parchment was in holes. And there was nothing, except a few faded lines which were unreadable, the inks had vanished. The surface was badly scratched, and there were faint grey ghosts of words which went in all directions on the page, as if it had been frequently turned around and used. It was from something like a copybook, she thought at last, a practice sheet for inkers, nothing more.

Along one margin was a faint, discoloured blob, where some careless hand had wiped the pen or shaken out ink. The page was a jumble of shadows, of pen strokes and lines. If only something had survived, to push through to the surface a complete sentence, even a single word appearing with sudden clarity. She took out her magnifying glass, but whatever had once been there could not be traced. Her eyes followed the margins opposite the rough edge where it must have been torn from the stitched folio. That blot annoyed her, its carelessness recalled the instructor who rapped the apprentice's knuckles. She held the magnifying glass closer. Then wondered if it was an accidental mark, there was something too regular about it, not a spill but a patch washed over with even brush strokes. It hid something which had long faded; the mark alone called attention to the secret.

She turned the page sideways and followed the direction of the folds. If only something remained, just a paragraph of the cramped minuscule showing through the insular script. In some lines the large square capitals seemed at war as unicals remained firmly in place from a previous text.

All she had were the marks of a scribe who cut deep into the surface. Fierce erasement of work, crossing out all else, and the furtive error that could not be concealed. It was probably a simple message, clear to the medieval student bent over the book with a candle, but impenetrable to her.

Perhaps it was a cabalistic work, a work of profanity and magic which the church authorities deemed worthless, or dangerous. A frugal order would have retained the base for the instruction of their newer scribes, setting them to practise on old vellum. Cecile ached to have had a glimpse of the book as it was originally. But there were no new clues to its past.

It was worthless, a useless scrap. She decided that she would take all three objects to the restorers the next time they were both in school. Her conscience was troubling her. Her secret preyed upon her mind. Last night she had dreamed of being alone. She should have been a hermit the way she rushed to her cubby hole. She revelled in solitude. The dream disturbed her. Impossible to shake off the image, she found herself looking up references to the practice. Hermits were believed to have healing powers, to be seers and visionaries. The faithful would travel great distances to listen to them preach from their cells. Some of them renounced speech as evil. That was what she would have done. She would never respond to requests to bless children or withered limbs.

Many nuns taught while in enclosure by remaining behind a wooden grille to address their audiences. A bending of the rules, but not unknown. Nuns rose to power and pre-eminence in the church through the visions and utterings they gave from God. Hildegard was consulted by the pope while others were forgotten. Who knows what was lost to the following generations, which saints were removed from the imagination, not only the church year. But no matter what she read, she kept an image in her mind, a dream which defied reason. A nun in matted robes, with grey dusty hair. A recluse who fought against her solitude, who pushed a bony hand through bars to be touched by the faithful who came to hear her, and, hermit no longer, walked free.

In the private library of the convent, locked into a glass case, was the large, bound book that contained early legal documents. There was a copy of the original charter granting their foundress the right to establish a community on church lands. It was a pompous document, ending with a great many signatures and seals.

Who were they, these long dead and forgotten church men? The document was of interest to no one except members of the community, to whom it was a cherished possession. Some of the statutes dated back to the sixteenth-century. They were glimpses into the routine life of the order, reminders of its constant nature. And bound into the same leather book were ancient bills and one fine example of commerce, a list of payments for work carried out after a fire destroyed the original abbey at Saumur in 1710. The community had moved, first southwards with a brief sojourn in northern Italy, and back to France with outreach convents being established. And all the time these documents travelled with them. The reason why their house retained the book was lost in history. A small number of nuns had taken refuge in Ireland, others in Spain during the Terror. The documents were believed to have been taken out of France around that time. Somehow they had worked their way to them.

Cecile, as chief librarian, had access to all the books. It was her great pleasure, and also her pain because she saw them left in terrible conditions. She chose the right key from her chain. As she opened the case the smell of mould was released.

The library was damp. Books were being destroyed. Only last week she had opened a reference work to find a delicate trace of silver worm across the frontispiece. She had asked repeatedly that something be done before the works were lost, for in that library were many peculiarities. There were the hand-written lives of the saints in beautiful copperplate, undertaken by a sister one hundred years ago, and the wonderful memories of one head of the Convent who in 1820 recorded the events of the church year. There were the codes of order, the copy of the *Rule* in Latin, and revised versions. Unfortunately there was no original version of the *Rule*. If there had been, it might have saved them from financial pressure. To them the item in itself was not valuable, only what it said. They lived the *Rule*, and had they been fortunate enough to have the vellum it was originally written on, it would have more than paid for restoration work.

Cecile asked to move those books in danger of further deterioration out of the damp library. As librarian she ought to have been empowered to do this, but Reverend Mother had not given permission and Cecile let the books rot.

She took out a heavy volume. Supporting it across her arm, she struggled to the nearest table. It was bound and fitted with a lock, the small key always left in place. The documents had still been kept as individual pieces as late as the nineteenth-century.

She turned the pages until she came to the part she wanted: the lists of bills and monies paid out. Her thin finger traced the lines, not touching the page, until at last she came to it. A copy receipt for the sale of land and some type of small building. The order had had a long struggle to clear itself of a debt inherited with land it was granted. On this land were the ruins of an earlier religious house. Although they appeared to have sold off most of the property, passing it into lay hands, still the debt had not been paid in full, 'pecunia in nominibus est'.

She thought back to the mark she saw on the parchment. Something was puzzling her, and was to keep her puzzled for a long time.

17

APPEARANCES

IN THE CONVENT THINGS were not right. There was something disconcerting about having men on the premises, Cecile felt it. Even with Father Armitage, the chaplain, there was a frisson as he passed in the corridor. It annoyed Cecile. Father Armitage. A grey, boring man. In the pulpit his preaching was uninspired. He was unable to engage the girls in any sort of discussion during class time. Whatever sparks had motivated him into the priesthood had long been extinguished. Impossible to imagine him filling one with enthusiasm, imparting joy in living God's calling. His was a dowdy version of religious life.

She learned, to her frustration, that he was a tiresome conversationalist whenever she met him on his rounds. He was quite unlike the monks of old, those brilliant rhetoricians of the middle ages who delighted in debate, who espoused friendship as the highest principle of human emotion and who were not too scathing about love. No, this was a slighter time.

Cecile knew that Mr Belli, the senior restorer, was too close to the girls' own fathers to create disturbances, but the other fellow, Wainsworth, he was young enough. To her mind he was not good looking, not a film star, but he was a man, not too old and reasonably fit. The Lord knows, he might be unorthodox enough to excite some of the girls. In the absence of men, who becomes God?

She remembered the disaster they had had the previous year with some of their fifth-years when the carpenters were putting in new cupboards in the lower-school library. The foreman complained to Reverend Mother that his apprentice was being hounded; not that the young boy minded, but the work was not getting done with him sneaking off every lunch break. He was meeting one of the girls in the park. Eventually they had to make the library out of bounds and announce at assembly that the parents of those girls who persisted in hanging around would be informed.

Then there was the episode with the sailors at the docks and those girls were only third-years. They could not have their pupils behaving in such a way. Girls needed to be watched for their own good. Cecile knew that. They were at that awful stage, not yet women and desperate to prove that they were.

Cecile knew that even the sixth-formers might be disturbed. Thank heaven for single-sex schools. Putting young girls through this disturbance daily would destroy any aptitude for work.

Once an extremely good-looking priest had come to lead the retreat. She had never seen so many eager to go to confession or take the sacraments. And the younger nuns had a liveliness about them which was missing at other times.

It was strange, this chemistry. Cecile had never experienced it. She cared little whether a person was male or female. It made no difference to her. She doubted if there was such a thing as a natural sex drive. She believed it was the product of too much television, trashy books and advertising. It was an artificially created sensation. But, artificial or not, she had noticed the numbers of girls who clustered around the chapel, waiting to catch a glimpse of that poor, slight man who thought of only his work. And it irritated Cecile, the disturbance caused by strangers among them.

For Wainsworth it was to be another day's work on the background, laboriously peeling off layers of varnish which were discoloured and dull with age. In the past the custodians of the painting had subjected it to heavy-handed treatment; old cracks were varnished over until the surface built up a fine exo-skeleton of crisp, opaque brown. In places it was so dense that no background detail showed at all. Wainsworth suspected that there would only be flat colour in much of these areas, a weak receding cast applied sparsely, yet his training made him take as much care as if he worked on the face of a saint.

He hated the smell of the alcohol solvent he was using. It was a mild mixture which removed a thin layer at a time, but it caught the back of his throat. He wondered if he was becoming allergic to turpentine. He would have to use a variety of mixtures for each layer as their compositions would be different. He sifted like an archeologist, discovering each stratum and guessing where he could.

He always imagined that one day he would find an early amber resin, the 'Vernice Liquida' of the queen who shaved her golden hair and presented it to Venus in thanks for the safe return of her king. But he knew he wouldn't. The painting was so mistreated he doubted anything remained under the darkened patches where the cracks had been glossed over.

The once hard film came away in brittle flakes first, then softer as the solvent continued to work. The smell was far removed from that of a woman's hair. It was a working smell, not the stuff of myths, but of docks and factories and warehouses. The smell of sandarac arriving from the African coast, the smell of industry; of pine trees, mastic and terebinth. This was the reality of resin. Rough labour to gloss the lightest touch upon a board, to hold still the fluttering pigments.

Venus took the queen's hair and wove it into the sky. It became the brightest band of stars by night. Wainsworth coughed. The sludge of yellow grime that came away irritated him.

One day he might find an original varnish, of amber mastic and Venetian turps. With resin of pines, galbanum, myrrh, gum, linseed and florae puppli. It would be like standing in the workshop on the day the varnish was mixed centuries ago. He would stand as the master heated the substance in a copper bowl, and the apprentice handled the bellows. A trained hand would carefully apply it when warm, pressing the varnish into the surface. As it dried it sealed in the dreams of artists, bound into a queen's bright hair.

He and Arturo had been peeling varnish for over a month now. A few corners of the panel were clear. He was impatient to start on the actual colour, the real restorative work, mixing and grinding pigment until the hue was as close a match as the human eye could understand. To see this dull panel restored to its original glory caused his heart to beat quickly, but no more so than when he imagined the old nun's delight. She could have no idea how beautiful it had once been.

These were the times when he was at perfect peace with himself and his surroundings, anticipating the eventual glory of the panel, the happiness it would give the community of nuns and the school. He knew the effect such a transformation would have. People did not realise the full splendour of images which were faded and buried under accumulated debris. It gave him real satisfaction to watch the simple pleasure of recognition as people discovered the new in the familiar.

He knew that the panel was spectacular when he first viewed it. Then he could scarcely contain his excitement, which was why he made sure that the department sent out the restraining hand of his senior colleague.

That first time in the chapel, his expert eye noticed tiny details. He saw how the saint stood in the open, at the scene of his execution, and he wondered if behind him there was an early landscape. There was some indication of grass and a small clump of trees, but it was so difficult to say what it might be until the coatings were removed. They might have been patterned tiles on the floor which were painted over, or a secondary image: a local figure, possibly the donor.

This panel was simple in construction, the pictorial imagery naïve. The saint occupied the central area, two thirds of the visual. There appeared to be no kneeling figures, unusual because they were normally clustered into a corner. This might have been the side panel of an altarpiece. The saint and the dove were the sole subjects of the panel. He wondered if it had been part of a series illustrating events in the saint's life. There would have been other sections. This could have been part of a triptych or another arrangement of images. Part of a grander altarpiece. The central area might have shown the saint received into Heaven, or the smaller panels could have all been different saints.

Sister Cecile had remarked to him that history was fragmented, just like the painting. She said the most frustrating thing was to find a story separated from its background, and not be able to go further with it.

'There are so many things we cannot know,' she said, shaking her head. He thought she wanted to talk, but she left him to continue, saying that he was to send for her as soon as anything new struck him. She seemed to be puzzling over something, and was uneasy.

This morning he waited until he saw that the last tenuous layer of varnish was beginning to dissolve. He should give Arturo a ring back at the museum and get him to come down. Sometimes he doubted his judgment in very fine areas and wanted his colleague to look over it before he continued. He did not want to find that he had wiped out years of work. He cleaned his hands, stopped work and walked towards the window of the ante-room which looked out onto the courtyard. Leaves were rotting in heaps where they had been gathered. It seemed as if the entire world was composed of decaying leaves, the turn of one season into the next, the decay of all living matter.

He watched the girls walk arm in arm. It was madness to think they would not always be there, walking and in conversation. He could not believe that such things ended, that life would not have its constancy.

The room was airless and he wanted to get out. His eyes,

rested by a minute's staring from the window, picked up a light patch in the painting which he had not noticed before. Something was showing through. He panicked; perhaps he had cleaned through to the base? He took out his eyeglass from the top pocket of his waistcoat. Squinting, he stared hard at the area. Carefully he shone the dilute beam from his fine spotlight on to the space. His eye picked out a faint stippling of colour. It was some of the original background painting, lighter and more luminous.

There was nothing recognisable. He took out the strongest lens he had and peered at the grey space, holding his breath lest the condensation he would cause by breathing might damage the tiny area of unprotected painting. He stood up and inhaled, then took a pocket handkerchief which he fixed across his mouth, wondering if he looked like a bank-robber. He emptied his lungs of air and bent again to continue inspection.

Like all such things, he thought it was imagined, that his eyes played tricks, that he was working too hard. Or that he saw it because he desired it and his eyes obediently lied. We fool ourselves, he thought, but he could see the glimmer under the varnish.

First it was a patch of pale grey, and his sober mind told him that it was not cause for excitement. But the grey ended abruptly and sky was never vertical. The pale patch shimmered and was indistinct.

He thought then it might be something of local significance, a rock formation, some massive boulder that stood near to the site, the end of a stretch of cliffs. A wealthy patron's request, depicting a local miracle, or a custom now lost.

He flicked off the light and his hands worked – even, rhythmic, monotonous – on the surrounding area. One slight, uncontrolled move and the patch would disappear just as the varnish had, rubbed out by carelessness.

That was the contradiction. His passion for the painting necessitated his restraint. Under his excited touch it would wither, and leave no trace of itself. Destroyed by his feelings.

His work was such that he ought not to leave an impression. His earnestness to see a painting revealed could force a different image to appear. One that the artist had not intended. He was ever vigilant in his own invisibility. In his best work he did not exist.

As he worked he was part of the painting. He felt if he put out his hand he would touch skin and hair, the leaves on trees, and feel the sharp cold of seawater. The day before he had the strangest sensation of seeing the back of the martyr's head, for he knew it to be quite bald and he saw the thin elongated spine of the saint. He knew he had only to look out from where he stood behind the saint to see himself. But he could not. And when he viewed the saint again, this time flat and staring out to face the viewer, he knew that the ground was muddy, and it disturbed him. He could smell the mouldering leaves as autumn passed into winter.

When the tower rose sharply from the background, it had waited so long to be discovered, entombed under layers of varnish, that it surfaced arrogantly, and it was as if he already knew or remembered something.

Peering through his eyeglass, he thought it had been painted over something: a tree or a gate. He did not like the way it loomed into the painting. It was not that he took a dislike to it for spoiling an uninterrupted view of the background. It was something even odder. It was a feeling he had, nothing more, a strange sensation that made him distrust it.

It was hard to work out if it was attached to something because it was situated outdoors. It stood on its own, away from any building. There were no ruins to suggest that it was part of a castle or church. Just a small tower, according to the artist. Maybe a siege won then forgotten.

'But I have seen that before.'

Cecile stood over the panel, covered her mouth with her hand and fixed it with a determined look. Wainsworth did not seem to hear.

'Well, you did ask me to send for you,' he remarked

distractedly. 'Although it's not much, I suspect there is something else under this varnish. Tomorrow my colleague will join me, I hope we will be able to show you something more interesting then.'

He had not heard her.

'I have seen this shape before, elsewhere.'

He looked at her. 'I'm sorry?' he said.

She did not know how much to tell him, but while she hesitated he continued talking.

'Ah, yes, the reliquary. You know I had a feeling that I recognised it too. Of course, that is carved into some sort of a tower isn't it?'

Cecile stared past him at the panel.

'This tower,' she said. 'This is the one I have seen.'

'Well,' the small man continued, 'the two were probably meant to represent the same thing. It must have been a local shrine, the site of a miracle. The reliquary would probably have contained bones of some saint, maybe a follower of Polycarp.'

Cecile knew that she would have to tell him what she had found. She beckoned him to come away from the panel and began to describe the three objects, how they had tumbled out, and how she had put them back carefully.

'It's the parchment that I can't make anything out of. So many writings and re-writings, so many marks and fadings, and the folding of it to let it fit inside. But it's the same tower.'

'We can never be sure of that, we can only guess. These are small things left over from someone's lifetime and might be of little significance. It does suggest that the artist was noting a place of pilgrimage though, badges and magic stones would all fit in with the description.'

'What ought I to do now?' Cecile asked him.

'Well, I don't think you should bother Reverend Mother with these things yet, not until we can present her with a hypothesis. We'll have to use a lot of guesswork. May I come tomorrow with Arturo to see the three things? I've asked him to come in to work on the rest of the background.'

The nun nodded. He looked secretive as if he wanted to giggle. They were like small children guilty with excitement.

But the next day Cecile was called back to the ante-room by a flushed Wainsworth.

'I said that the grey building was not everything,' he said walking quickly so that the old nun had to run every few steps.

In the chapel Arturo flapped his arms and put his hands to his lips like a conspirator, but it was only to warn her to cover her nose and mouth before going to see. Wainsworth gave her a folded handkerchief and with this in place she let them take her in.

The background had been cleared, the dull brown removed right up to the top corner where the old frame had obscured part of the surface. But it had also preserved it, for under the dark shadow and the impression of the wood, Cecile could see a group of figures.

'Three,' the big man said. 'Three standing figures. We have been able to clean the area and can make them out. They're still quite faint. I think a later hand added them.'

'Might they not be donors?' Cecile asked.

'It would not be usual to hide them in this way. No, these have been added after. I think someone who owned the painting might have asked to have a local event included. Obviously the characters had limited significance – probably part of a folk legend.' He turned to his colleague. 'What do you think?'

'Well they look like they are from a religious order. This figure,' he pointed to the one on the far left, 'this is undoubtedly a nun, but this,' he indicated a taller form, 'could be either a monk or a lay man. It's hard to tell, they're so small and so indistinct. It's not a female – while the third is certainly a young girl or a child.'

Dressed in white, standing between the two, was a smaller figure. Some indication of hair, which was long and loose confirmed its gender.

'It must have been a popular story at the time; a monk, a nun and their child. It was a common theme. Then again it could be the child with her guardians, or teachers. There's a lot of room for interpretation. This figure might not be a monk at all, and that silent tower further back, who knows? It's a painting full of questions at which we can only guess.'

Wainsworth did not like to voice an opinion, but he felt with a certainty which surprised him, that the man was no monk, rather a man who teetered on the brink.

Cecile using Wainsworth's eyeglass to study the figures was equally certain that the nun was a teacher. She had no idea why. But with so little to go on, anything could be speculated upon with conviction.

Siobhan stood in front of the wardrobe mirror so that she could see her entire body, and she looked at it imagining how it might feel when it no longer belonged to her, but had been offered up via the convent. Would she say a final goodbye? Would her feelings change towards herself? She might feel invisible under the habit of a nun.

She looked at herself knowing that some day she would not have the right to look or to want to make herself appear a certain way. She turned sideways to the mirror and stared at her belly – a faint bulb of skin which showed beneath her rib cage.

Was it a sin to look at herself this way? Soon it might be. She needed to say her own farewell to everything she would not take with her as she started her new life. She would be reborn, out of the physical into the spiritual. It felt suddenly very final, like a cutting off. It made her retch. Quickly she put her dressing gown on. Its brown and beige checks enveloped her and reached down to her bare feet. She took up the towel she had used to dry her hair. She blotted the dripping ends and as she did so she had the feeling that it too would one day be a last event for her.

She wondered how they managed in the convent. Did they

all keep their hair a uniform shortness? She supposed that there were days when it was permitted to wash their hair, and times it was not. She remembered her own father making a fuss one Easter Sunday when her mother had bathed her and brought her down into the only warm room to have her hair dried in front of the fire.

It was freezing. She was six years old and felt contented. She had a huge chocolate egg on the sideboard. After the torture of Lent the world could offer no greater reward for goodness than the sweet, thick chocolate melting on her tongue.

It was morning. Her mother told her that the Pope would be giving the papal blessing in Saint Peter's Square. One day she would go there to receive it, travel to Rome and stand within sight of the great father's hand.

That morning like all Easter mornings, they would go to eleven o'clock mass and eat a late breakfast, while out of the corner of her eye the chocolate egg would tease her.

'You give thanks for Christ's resurrection first, for the signs of hope, for the truth that man can triumph over death. That's what Easter is about,' her father said.

There were those who consumed their eggs with indecent haste. Those who woke on Sunday morning and took their egg, to eat pieces of it between the warmth of their blankets. It sounded good to her.

Her mother used to set the vacuum cleaner to blow and make her sit in front of the jet of air. It made a terrible noise. Impossible to hear the hymns being sung on the television. Suddenly her father was on his feet, shouting and swearing that this was not the time or the day of the week to do such things.

'Are you a bloody heathen or what? You're getting the kid into your habits now!' and he stormed around the room, because his peaceful Sunday morning had been disturbed by the sight of a not yet dressed child.

'On a Sunday! And Easter Sunday at that!'

Siobhan began to cry, for she had committed a terrible sin. Her mother shouted.

'When else can I do it? Go on, you tell us when there's time? On Saturday I'm too bloody busy. The rest of the week she's at school. It takes too long to heat enough water to fill that sodding iron bath in the evening. You pick a decent Catholic time, you hypocrite!'

She walked away, leaving her with a wet head, crying and shivering in the thin towel. She crouched behind the armchair. Her father stared at the television. In Rome the Pope was giving his message of peace to the Catholic nation.

'Stop snivelling!' he yelled. 'Jesus! Can't I have any comfort!'

Her mother put her head round the door and screamed at her to get out.

In the dark unheated corridor she trembled. Her despicable hair dripped. A sneeze and her mother grew wild.

'If she gets the flu on account of this, I'm going up to that priest, I'm going to tell him how you carry on!' she shouted through the door. 'You miserable bastard, the kid has to stand outside because . . .' but she couldn't finish the sentence, she snorted and choked.

Siobhan knew she was guilty of something awful. She cried and her mother hit her. Her father stormed out and swiped a blow at her and told her to keep quiet. He shook his head. She was not the trouble free, clean child he could be proud of who spoke when she was spoken to and never disagreed, wearing exact replicas of her parents' clothing and walking in the same way.

Once she had seen a woman with her daughter. They wore identical clothes, twin sets and pearls. Fakes. Their hair gripped back in the same alice-bands. The girl was maybe twelve, yet she wore a copy of her mother's outfit, could have remained in the same style into her fifties. The overshadow of the parent, reproducing itself, to control the young shoot. It gave her the creeps. She was always trying to do everything the opposite to her family.

Maybe that was why she had this religious rush – this fervour which had planted itself in her to spite her parents with their everyday ritual obedience to a God without feeling.

She let the towel drape around her shoulders, then on an impulse she quickly pulled it over her head to let it hang flatly as a veil or headdress might. She watched herself in the mirror. She did not make a convincing nun.

She turned her head, wondering which profile was the best, the most devout, or the most compassionate. She imagined herself coming back to her family, grown up, her father white-haired. She would put her hands on him and the neighbours would say what a saint she was to be so forgiving.

She imagined her mother, trying to explain away the trouble they once had with their daughter. Neighbours would remark how they always knew she was different, how they knew she had a mission to accomplish, how she wanted her own life, and how, despite the opposition, she had stuck out for what she believed was correct.

She no longer knew what she believed in. It was as if God was dressing up to frighten her father. She did not know what she wanted of religion, but she wanted an escape from the life she had been shown. She wanted a life like other people. Like the girls in her class who did not dread going home. But she faced an eternal argument, never to be resolved as long as she stayed. She knew that the convent would show her a way out, and it was her only escape.

18

INTERVIEW

WHEN CECILE MET THE Doolins they were polite to the point of ridiculous. Neither saw her at the window, but she had watched them as they crossed the gravel path towards the main door of the convent. Mr Doolin strode in front of his wife who broke into small trotting steps to keep up. He did not once slow down.

In the office he was murderously polite. He held the chair back for Mrs Doolin and waited stiffly until both women were seated before he lowered himself on to the rickety school chair that had been carried into Reverend Mother's office for the interview.

Of the two, Mrs Doolin appeared the more nervous. She did not speak beyond the initial exchange of pleasantries and comments about the weather. But the man became pompous as if he had made up his mind to show that he was not a man without brain power. He was too eager to ask the ready question, the set piece he had formulated which needed no answer but was a vehicle for him to convey his knowledge.

Cecile did not speak her fears for Siobhan, but began gently with a remark that their daughter's work was not up to her usual standard. She prodded them for information. Could they suggest what had changed her? Had they noticed anything about her behaviour at home?

'Her concentration is particularly wayward of late . . .'

Mrs Doolin glanced up then returned to staring at the

hands in her lap. She twisted her fingers and played with her wedding ring, turning it round the plump finger of her left hand.

'I've noticed that her homework is not given in as regularly as it was. It's often a day late. It used to be always there on my desk in plenty of time. It's not that anything drastic has happened, but I am concerned at this drop in standards in a girl who usually takes more care. She has made such an improvement since the start of this school year that I'm worried she might be slipping back. I cannot stress how important this first year of the exam course is. This is when we lay the foundations for the qualifications the girls ought to pick up at the end of their sixth form. Losing interest now, for whatever reason, could mean disaster next June.'

Mr Doolin was nodding. His wife sat without moving except for the fearsome activity of her hands. Cecile was unable to inject any warmth into her voice or help them relax. She sensed the massive space between them and when she looked at the man, all compassion seemed to leave her. They were so alien. He was still nodding while she was sure he rehearsed some phrase that was meant to impress, not to solve or come to terms with what she said.

'I'll make sure she doesn't get away with that kind of behaviour. Don't you worry, I'll take a firm hand to her at home. I don't let her get away with bad behaviour, I'll not have her being disrespectful to her elders. Not giving her homework in on time. Just who does she think she is? She thinks we can wait around for her does she, getting high and mighty is she, eh? I'll see about that!'

Cecile watched his wife squirm. This interview wasn't fair. The entire thing wasn't fair. She had arranged this in order to observe them like exhibits in the biology lab, spread open, their outer skins pinned back, so she could inspect the smallest detail. No doubt they were decent, hard-working people. She could respect that, but not the reality in front of her which was awkward and on its best behaviour. The three sat silently like travellers who meet in a waiting room, each listening for the platform call and glad when it sounds to send them to their different destinations, out of that strange limbo between trains.

Suddenly she wanted the interview to be over. She felt she understood. What she suspected was correct and she, if anything, had made it worse.

'It's not a question of behaviour,' she spoke quickly wanting to recover. 'On the contrary I always find Siobhan to be a most willing and helpful pupil. She is the last girl I would recommend her parents taking a . . . firm hand to . . . as you suggest. I wondered if it might be something else?'

The two looked blankly at her.

'Could she be upset over something? Is there something you are aware of that could have caused your daughter to become unsettled? Some row with a boy? A friend?'

Mr Doolin pulled himself up in the chair; his chest swelled.

'We don't let her have anything to do with boys, not at her age, carrying on like that . . .' his voice trailed off in disgust.

'I did not mean to suggest . . .'

'If it's boys,' he cut in, 'if that's what all this is about I'll see to it, I'll not stand for anything like that, at her age . . .'

Cecile felt the situation was getting worse. She was not managing the interview. Mrs Doolin looked shocked while her husband struggled to regain his composure. He was as angry as he might allow himself to become in public. Cecile wondered how he would behave in private once the controlling eye of the interviewer was removed. She sat back in her chair and took deep breaths to steady herself.

'Adolescence can be a difficult time for everyone involved. I can appreciate how hard it is for parents.' She tried to smile. 'After all, we only have to put up with them during the day, you have to live with them. But frankly Siobhan is not what I would call one of our problems, and we have many of those, indeed we do.' She caught Mrs Doolin's eye, and managed a stage laugh. It worked, the woman laughed back. Cecile raced on, scared to lose the moment.

'We see so many families here, so many problems at home. No family is unique. I hear repeated every year the same things which make life difficult for everyone. Believe me, there's nothing new. But please don't think that I called you in to criticise Siobhan. I would hate you to go away with the wrong idea. On the contrary I called you in to ascertain whether we might be able to help her.

'She is one of our more gifted pupils; normally well motivated. I've been pleased with the progress she's made. I'm concerned that she be allowed to progress, that nothing hampers her chance of success. Does she have somewhere to study at home? Her own room? If that's a problem we can arrange for her to have space here after school.'

'She spends a lot of time at school as it is,' Mrs Doolin began, but did not finish.

'Sometimes school offers an escape,' Cecile ventured then regretted her words as Mr Doolin's voice became sharp.

'Escape! What does she need to escape from?'

'At that age, young people want to spread their wings . . .' but she knew it sounded weak.

'There's too much of this freedom lark if you ask me. I don't know what it's all coming to.' He jabbed a thumb towards his wife. 'She never carried on the way these young girls do today. She was at home until we got married. The way it ought to be.'

Cecile often wondered if the scholarship method only created as many problems as it was supposed to solve. Throwing girls from different backgrounds together was difficult enough. Plunging the families into another world, and giving children expectations seemed at times impossible.

'Things change,' she said lamely.

Mrs Doolin attempted to whisper to her husband, but as that proved difficult and Cecile was not prepared to look away she was forced into speech.

'If she'd leave school, get a job, look after herself, then life would be easier ... I can't be doing with her at home the way she is ... I just ...' The shock of speaking made her eyes run, they filled with nervous tears and she pulled out a handkerchief. She blew her nose loudly and could not finish her sentence. Mr Doolin spoke roughly to her, warned her to control herself.

'It's like this,' he began, the reasonable man about to give a reasonable explanation. Cecile felt her jaw tighten.

'My wife and Siobhan do not get along. I'm afraid there are some arguments at home.' He turned to look at his wife and laughed a neat, short laugh. His wife's mouth gaped.

He turned towards Cecile, drawing her into his confidence, he smiled.

'You see, Sister, unlike us, my wife has no idea what it feels like to return home after a day's work at a responsible job.' The contempt in his voice was no longer hidden. 'She has no idea of what it is to work all day and want some peace at the end of it. I'm sure you can appreciate that. Honestly, sometimes the way they go at each other like hammer and tongs. It's as much as I can bear to be in the same room as them.' He shook his head, the wise father reprimanding his children.

Cecile did not trust wise fathers. Her own had been far too wise than was good for her. She hoped her face would not communicate anything. She tried to keep it mask-like. She looked away. Then she heard in the silence that funny little laugh, artificial as clearing the throat. When she looked at him he was attempting a smile in the direction of his wife. An open smile, like a letter to *The Times*; a smile to illustrate how reasonable he was, a smile to put everything into perspective – this too silly discussion. And he was really amused at his wife's arguments with his troublesome daughter. She could see that, couldn't she, by the way he smiled?

His wife rose from her chair, the legs scraped and caught the rug which remained twisted underfoot. A woman normally annoyed by such details, a tidy woman, she stood in front of them and sobbed.

'You have no right to blame me.'

In the still study her voice tore at the politeness surrounding them. Her voice ripped it into small pieces so tiny they could not be reassembled. She was lost to her usual, silent outer self.

'I'm not going to sit here a minute longer and watch you charm your way out of this one, you hypocrite!'

She wagged a fist at his face. Cecile could feel her rage. What would she have loved to do? Punch him, or was it merely to be threatening that she made the fist, was that enough for her?

'I can't sit here and be blamed for everything that's gone wrong. It's not fair. You're as much to blame. You're the one that hits her . . .' She covered her mouth quickly, terrified of what she had said, and collapsed back into the chair.

His face was white.

'Remember where you are,' he said.

There was silence. He was upright in the seat while his wife slumped in hers and held her head in her hands. She had exposed herself, but he still presented his hard front to the world.

Cecile knew her suspicions were correct.

'Well,' she said flatly. 'Is there anything more to say?'

As far as she was concerned the interview was over. She knew why Siobhan seemed so hurt. Not the physical knocks, she understood that they were the superficial grazes, visible marks which healed. No, they were not the problem in themselves. The damage that was being done to the girl's soul was what she feared most. It was being pulled and stretched and might warp hopelessly one day.

Mr Doolin was speaking again. She did not want to listen. She stood up to indicate that the interview was over, but his voice continued. She could not catch what he said, he spoke in a lower voice, his tone softer. It irritated her, she would have to pay attention just to hear the words; words she had no further interest in. She listened and was shocked. He spoke with a dignity she had not recognised before. This man stripped of pretensions, spoke simply.

'All I want is the best for her ...' his head dropped. She believed him.

'I want her to be something.' He looked up and met her eyes. 'Can you see that? I want her to go further than I ever could. And I'm scared of her sometimes. You know, I used to be able to talk to her, but lately she's changed. I know she thinks I'm a fool. I'm not educated enough.'

Cecile would have sympathised but the sight of the woman he had treated like a fool for years who was slumped behind him in a chair, hardened her.

'Do you know that she is contemplating a religious vocation?' The woman looked horrified.

'She will need a lot of time to think everything through. None of us wants her to make a mistake that she will spend the rest of her life regretting.'

She shook hands with them and watched them go. She ought to have felt relieved. She knew unhappiness was not enough for a religious vocation. Siobhan must convince her of something more. Anyone could rush away from their tangled families. The girl was religious. Of that there was no doubt. She was also desperate for affection. But that alone did not provide someone with the right credentials. It was not that easy to offer up a life to God. She had realised that.

19

BREAKING SILENCE

'I DON'T CARE, IT'S ridiculous, a waste of life,' her mother shouted.

Her mother, so hard a woman, looked close to tears. But they were tears of rage not compassion.

'You selfish cow, all you think about is yourself!'

From the other side of the room her mother threw knives and forks on to the table. They crashed painfully.

The girl was motionless. She would not speak. It had taken all her strength to make her announcement. She was rigid with fright and stared ahead, seeing only what passed in front of her eyes. Behind she heard her father sucking air, the sign of his exasperation.

'You little bitch.'

She grew cold as his enormous bulk cast its icy shadow. He was always telling her what to do. But it was more than interference, she could tell. He wanted to live through her life. Not content with his own he would use hers, suck it up to realise the lost ambitions of his past. But she wouldn't have that. His plans for her would open a grave instead of a future.

When she was small there was a game she used to play which always began by asking God what she was being punished for. She used to pretend she was a martyr. After the ritual death she would stand very still, imagining how the sky opened to make way for her. Then a saint took her hand and led her into paradise. It did not bother her that she left her parents behind. Even then she had dreamed of escape, of casting off everything like a worn-out shoe.

Every day at home for as long as she could remember there had been a row. If not between her mother and father, a shouting match aimed at her. Her stomach would contract with the first raised voice.

Habit should have made her impervious, instead it made her fearful. She became increasingly disturbed by arguments. Her parents were constructing an edifice. Burying her alive.

After, when the house sank back into irritable silence, she felt as if a sharp blade dug into her still.

'I've never heard anything so selfish,' her father's voice was raised. 'After everything we've done for you. I thought you had sense. I should have listened to your mother and got you out of that school. All that education wasted . . . I had hopes! . . .'

He put his large hands together and squeezed the air from between them. She had extinguished his dream. She might have felt pity, but the sight of him, red-faced and shouting, turned her feelings to disgust.

Yet she doubted her resolve. She would go away. The ceremony, as binding as a legal document, would deny them any rights. No longer their daughter she would begin another life, a new person with a new home.

'And what will you do?' her mother spat.

'All that studying just to be sent off to some God-forsaken hole somewhere as a missionary. They'll wear you out and you'll die forgotten in a strange country. Is that what you want?'

Siobhan couldn't move, couldn't shrug, she was paralysed.

'You're too young to make a decision like that. You're still a child. I'll make sure you can't do it. I'll go down to the office and tell them some truths. I'll not give my permission.'

Her father shook his head.

'Oh God, Alice. When will you ever understand?' His anger turned towards his wife.

He knew that their actions were hopeless. Siobhan had recently turned eighteen. She could do as she liked without their signature on anything. The year before even the voting age had been lowered. Now adulthood started earlier.

Her mother looked at him irritably. She was determined to do something, even if it was only a letter sent to the school.

She had no other way of getting back at her. She was as powerless as Siobhan had been most of her life against him. The girl was going to escape at last. She was going to remove herself so completely from them that they might never reach her.

'Just what the hell will the neighbours say?' her mother wailed. 'We had hopes for you.'

Siobhan knew what her mother's hopes were. Hopes of sticking her behind a counter, or into any job that came along. Her hopes were for the quick wage packet handed over unopened every Thursday. The woman of the house, in charge of the dutiful child who never grew up. Those were her mother's dreams, after all, that had been her mother's life and why should it be different for anyone else?

And after a few years, she might agree to her marrying someone, after she vetted them to make sure they were suitable. Suitable meant having a steady job. All other considerations paled compared to this. Given her mother's approval she would be expected to leap at this one chance, give up the lousy life of shop-assistant and take on the life of housewife.

'I had hopes for you,' her father spoke slowly. Words were difficult to form because he spoke the truth, and that came from the distant place, still and quiet where dreams took shape. They lay undisturbed, but now he pulled them out into daylight, and they were only half formed, raw and bloody without a chance of survival.

She wanted to say she was sorry, but knew her mother would scream that she might as well be. In her family sorrow was taken as weakness, remorse meant you had gone soft. But already her eyes filled with tears. Just when she wanted most to be hard.

'I thought that I ought to inform you of my decision,' she said.

'You stuck up little madam!' Her mother's hand came down flat across her cheek. 'You little bitch!' again she struck her.

Her father was shocked. 'There's no need for language like that.'

His voice was tight with disapproval. His wife turned to him and waved him away.

'Oh sod off Holy Joe. It's you that's got her like this, bloody Holy Joe.'

She spun round and swiped Siobhan. She was no longer her mother, but a screaming woman the girl did not recognise.

'Bitch! Little snob!'

Siobhan felt snot and tears run into her mouth. She put out her tongue and licked.

Her father clutched his chest uncertainly, his hands opened helplessly. His eyes bulged. He did not know this woman. He had never seen this foulness. His wife kicked the sink edge. It was as if she wanted to kill. The girl was straight like a statue, her face drained of life as saliva trickled from her mouth. Stop. Surely it was time to stop.

The girl made no sound. She was terrified, but could not walk away, just as she could not lift her hands to shield herself. The blows became weaker, her mother's strength was spent. The woman grunted with effort to bring her hand down across Siobhan's face. She looked like she was having a fit, like someone in the throes of madness.

'For God's sake stop ... stop ...' her father spluttered. After a lifetime of striking he was being made to watch. It disturbed him, not the anger, but the way his daughter stood her ground. She was resigned to it, accustomed through habit, and he was a witness; suddenly, no longer active he was a bystander. Always worse to watch.

He retched. Felt a pain in his chest. Focused, and saw

his wife's shaking hands which became claws as she waved them in front of her face. She was unstoppable. She breathed savagely. He feared her.

She was reckless. She hated everything. To hell with him, and with her. She was no daughter, yet their only daughter. Her daughter. She would frighten him. She did not care how. She was lower than the gutter. That's what he had meant when he reminded her that he took her from nothing, that she was wasting her life until he found her and pulled her up. Through him she had status. Her saviour. But she was decent, a decent woman. She spat her words.

'You're going to be so decent, Miss! Well, tell everyone that you're a bastard! That will take the wind out of your sails.' She looked to where he leaned against the wall. His eyes were two black points.

She arched her eyebrows. 'Him?' her voice was scornful. She cocked her head on one side. 'Him?'

Siobhan was shaking. Shock flowering like bruises. Her mouth opened. In the room her mother screamed.

'Look at her!' her voice so shrill it was hard to hear.

His glasses were askew, streaked with grease. He no longer knew what he saw.

'Does she look like you? Does she?'

Siobhan imagined that just then she must have looked like no one living.

'She hasn't got your eyes, she hasn't got your hair. Who do you think she looks like? No one you know. You're so sure of your tight, safe family aren't you? So sure of all of us. You'd be off your head to suspect me. I'm a good Catholic mother. I'm in church every Sunday. Now do you see why you can't treat her the way you do? Stop treating her like your own, because she isn't. Do you hear me? She isn't. Don't you ever lay a hand on her. That's the right of parents, and you . . . you're nothing . . .' She gulped and covered her face.

'Oh God, God, I've made it worse,' she moaned. 'I've done more harm today, and you forced me into this. You and your bullying. What have I done . . .' she cried loudly. 'What have I done?'

He felt another sharp pain in his chest, stronger this time, more urgent. His glasses fell sideways and hung from one ear. He made no move to retrieve them. Everything blurred. And the statue was bleeding. Another miracle.

The statue was white and small. Years later he would remember it and tell people that he once saw it bleed. He slumped down the wall. His mouth opened as though he wanted to speak, but no words came. In fact there was nothing to break the stillness and the complete dark which swallowed him as he felt a third and sudden pain.

PART FIVE

SPLINTERS

20

ILLNESS

HER HAIR WAS PALEST gold. When she was a baby they remarked how in sunlight it looked pink. Then it stuck out wildly from the crown, tangled by the rubbing of her head against the sheep's fleece. Fine baby-hair which coarsened as she grew, and she became known as Pinnosa.

At first glance her eyes were colourless; deceptive because they absorbed colour, reflected this in the absence of a true self. At times the child's eyes seemed black when the pupils were widest, in bright day they shrunk to the tiniest dot and her eyes would flood with the green of pasture, the yellow of candlesticks or the grey impermanence of clouds.

She was the palest trace of a baby. At first they thought she would fade, as if the tiny thing sensed that its claim to life was tenuous. The infirmarian sat up many nights as the sickly thing fought to keep a hold on life. Many times the infirmarian wondered whether to call the order to prayer as she listened to its patchy breathing, waited for the thrub of a heartbeat.

By her first year the child had toughened. Her body weathered to suit the climate. She adapted and her bones grew straight even if she wanted at times for food. The child listened and understood the ways of her world. She learned to expect times of hunger, times of pain. She grew through hardship and was graceful.

She observed the world. She had no mother, nor knowledge

of what it was to be the daughter of woman. She was without beginning in this place.

She was alone. She was among the sisters, but not yet one of them. As a child she would run crying to the kindly old nun who kept the infirmary. Each day she watched Gertrude as she locked away the medicines in the wooden trunk with its heavy device for triple locking.

'Medicines are poisons,' Gertrude would tell her as she bent with the great key. 'Always treat them with respect.'

Everything was to be signed for, everything must be approved by the abbess. The infirmarian could not even make a poultice without her say-so. Gertrude even asked for permission to use the comfrey which grew in abundance in the fields.

As soon as she reached the age of six summers the child joined the rest of the order four times a year with a cupping bowl for Sister Gertrude to leach or scarify. Sister Gertrude insisted on flebotomy: she believed in its virtues to keep the order healthy in body as well as mind. Often with bruises and cuts she was taken by Gertrude and pieces of inscribed parchment with holy charms were tied around her sores. The infirmarian kept the magic stones in a drawer with a stock of holy water phials for bathing afflicted parts. Pinnosa did not learn what the old metal implements which hung in racks were for. They were never used, but remained, forgotten and rusting.

Gertrude said the best remedy for all ills was prayer. She did not encourage moon-watching, and told the child that there was nothing significant in the phases she could see in the night skies.

So Pinnosa learned; she knew that tears were weakness, that running was to abuse the body, that her appetite was to be chastened, that her body was the receptacle of the Devil and must be properly guarded. She learned to train her mind upon God's love, but she did not learn what the ache in her heart was. Sister Gertrude had no magic stone which might remove that. She continued to grow, and at times experienced a sadness which caught her unawares.

These were the times she would ask Gertrude how she came to the convent. But the old nun had no answer. Sometimes she shook her head sadly and seemed to remember a detail which made her join in Pinnosa's mood, other times she said that it was not known.

Pinnosa did not understand how she was part of the convent school yet different. She was treated as if she came from a high rank yet no one could tell her about her parents and she did not believe she had any, for she had been told that she was without a beginning.

Yet she was to be no lay sister, unlike the convent children, who were trained to maintain the house, to work and clean, leaving the nuns free to contemplate God and pray for the sins of the world.

When she was small, Gertrude made up tales to ease the empty spaces in her history. Epics which took up the long hours before choir. Then Pinnosa would delight to hear how she had arrived in a silver boat that was storm tossed upon the ocean, how she had fallen to them from the sky on a night like pitch when the wet sky cracked.

Then her eyes were as black as the sky of her imagination and she would demand more, yet more. But Gertrude had nothing to show her that marked her arrival, and Pinnosa knew at last that all was invention.

She developed a special devotion to the Virgin Mother of God who could be her mother too. She went to the kitchen sister when she wanted an extra piece of bread, to the infirmarian when she stumbled over a tree root and wanted comforting. These women were all her mothers.

The abbess alone terrified her. She it was who stopped her association with Gertrude, saying that her head was stuffed with nonsense, dangerous nonsense. Ever after, Pinnosa set her face and went about her tasks bravely ignoring the heartbroken nun who waited to see her as she walked out. Pinnosa prayed to have her sin forgiven. She feared the cold, silent abbess.

In her fourteenth year she made the transition to postulant.

This and her skill with a pen took her to Werberga to be trained. She was disciplined, she no longer needed a mother. In the icy scriptorium she spent long days, copying the words in front of her. Werberga would train her to illuminate, she was to be more than a copyist. She asked for forgiveness for her conceit when they said she had the delicacy of touch required.

The abbess was tormented when she heard of Pinnosa's progress. Always hard on the child, she could not hear good of her without suffering the unbearable anguish of misplaced pride.

Gertrude, her health broken, understood and did not feel the abbess was unduly hard, even if her actions had seemed so.

'There is no sin to rejoice in one's sister's achievement,' she said to Aelreda. 'A little more rejoicing in what we can achieve, a little more delight in each other's ability might help us appreciate God's goodness. These gifts are given for a purpose.'

The abbess always bowed to Gertrude's greater years. The old nun had witnessed much in her life.

'You speak to ease my heart, kind Sister Gertrude. But we must be ever on our guard against such feelings for our sisters. Such intense personal pleasure in any one . . . do you forget such a liaison between two postulants of our order?' She shook her head sadly.

'From such mistakes we learn. We must control our feelings. Not run wild with them. We must be vigilant.'

'We ought to delight in God's world,' the old nun said. But the abbess shuddered, disturbed by memory.

The Year of Our Lord 921

Written this day by God's good grace. I am taken over by this task. Fine straight lines I make for his glory. No one heeds me, I am left to work. A fine book I have discovered, unfinished. If I had the skill to complete such a work, but I scarce understand what is written there. Werberga allows me to ink in those figures she has placed inside a grid. But not the gold leafing which I delighted in too much and sinned by eagerness so that my vain hand was led into luxury and wantonness. The page was spoiled and I, Pinnosa, miserable wretch, now serve my long apprenticeship.

The Year of Our Lord 923

Glory be to God, the Father and Son and creator of all living things. God, who created me, instruct me, show me the right way.

Faster now my hand flies across the page. The margins are my spaces for the silences that fill the day. Into gaps is my story written. I, who have no memory, who am known as Pinnosa, have no beginning. Like the tower in the chapel, standing silent as it always has. No one will tell me why it is there. It is a mystery, it is my mystery. Carefully I draw it in along the edge. My sign. Silent as I am.

The Convent of Fortitude. The Year of Our Lord 924

Werberga, scribe to the order, makes this page in humble love of God. For our sins so shall we suffer.

And after such a hard frost, the terrible winter of dark and ice behind us, yet we fear it should bid us anew. There has been a shrivelling of crops, a drying of the earth's belly and the land is barren. Clean earth brought famine, after pestilence burned. By the grace of God's mercy we, remaining in our walls and safe from greater intercourse, were spared. But three of our sisters were afflicted at a time of great loss everywhere. With sweating sickness and flux, then boils appeared under their arms and in places privy to the body. Pink hard swellings which did burst with stinking matter.

Our losses might be slight. But in those places where men congregate without room to walk freely, where they pack together and their houses lean in sweating intimacy; in these places the pestilence might pass easy, in and out of doors which are left open and welcoming.

*In our order, three afflicted, and two of these shall soon be
taken from us. Our good sister Gertrude waits to give the rattle to
prayer, still leaving food at their doors, pushing this towards them
in bowls.*

And none of us know if sadness shall befall us.

The scribe moved with difficulty. She was stiff from sitting so
long bent over her desk top, and her joints cracked. She flexed
her fingers to ease the cramp where she held the pen and shook
out her hand, her working hand which was blessed by God. The
page she worked was pegged tightly to the raised table on her
desk. She was not satisfied with it. It lacked movement even
if it was just a simple outline which another hand would ink.

They had a reputation for possessing many books. But
Werberga knew that the sisters she recruited as scribes and
copyists were unsuitable. They were clumsy and handled the
dyes carelessly. She saw how they inked in solid areas like
people sleeping, their minds not on the work. Now they produced books, but Werberga was not pleased with the quality.
She had grown old building up their library. It was Aelreda's
idea, that this convent would increase in importance if they
could develop a skill, have a reputation.

Some days Werberga dreaded entering the scriptorium. She
cast her eyes the length of it now. Empty. This was how she
wanted it to be, instead of the busy area it had become during
the work period.

She was tired with trying to control the overall appearance
of a work. She would make sure that any book at least had a
frontispiece that bore some reasonable decoration. Only that
day she had shouted at a copyist: 'No, no! Not like that! Try
light sweeping strokes. Twist the brush on the upstroke, that
is what makes the line narrow. Turn it again for a thicker stroke.'

That novice had not even been trained to rule margins
yet the abbess sent her to work in the scriptorium.

It was a difficult time indeed, now that they had lost their
one good apprentice. Of all those she trained over the last

twelve months, few showed promise. Pinnosa's script could be trusted. She did not repeat mistakes, but stopped and queried where the less able worked on, copying errors and magnifying them with their dull wits. But all that day Pinnosa's place had been empty.

Werberga waited in the morning as the novices took up their seats. The scriptorium roof was high and because of the many apertures for light it was always draughty and cold, but better than working in the cloisters, where now only inkers worked. Werberga was used to it but the newest recruits shivered and were allowed to bring their heavy outdoor cloaks to wrap themselves as they worked. There had only been six. They worked silently with their heads down, yet all knew Pinnosa was absent. Each day a scribe produced half a page of basic text on the yellow vellum which was all they could now obtain.

They had copies of *Augustine's Confessions* and *De Trinitate* and a small *Lives of the Saints*. But Werberga knew the novices copied blindly and she worried that the books could be riddled with faults. God's immutable law altered by the slip of a pen, the nature of the universe changed by a misspelling, passed down intact to another generation of readers. Each evening she corrected their work with neat upright strokes, lest their library became infamous for heretical works rather than for any branch of learning.

She planned to talk to her abbess, somehow put a stop to what was happening and begin again, slowly, with proper training, to build up a steady stream of work. A library was the work of many lifetimes, needing longer than any human span of time.

It would outlive her, just as it would outlive Pinnosa who lay isolated from the main body of the convent. She was in a dream which would last for days, unaware that two of her sisters had succumbed already and she was set to follow them into eternal sleep. At times she was hot, when the fever burned, then she would shiver so violently it was as if she was surrounded by snow. Gertrude seemed to care little whether she survived

Pinnosa. As the fever broke the old nun had entered the long room where all three sick had once lain together. Only Pinnosa remained. They all knew that soon Gertrude would take down the rattle again and call the sisters to pray for their dear sister's soul. It was hopeless to imagine that death could be postponed, even as the old nun applied cold pads to the white forehead, wanting to ease the suffering in any way she could. She spent the days watching Pinnosa helplessly, who slept or woke to recognise no one.

21

IMAGINATION

Siobhan was a dreamer. She knew it but did not know any other way of being. At school she was criticised, but no one ever told her how to stop, gave her guidelines on how not to do it. If she did not dream, what was she supposed to do instead? She tried throughout her schooling to stop; to spend a morning looking at the hard-edged faces in the class room, the sharp chin of Miss Cameron in the science laboratory who used to stare at her down the length of a test tube.

'What do you mean, you didn't hear me tell the class to put in the zinc?'

Her experiment was ruined, the contents of her glass tube alone dark brown in a laboratory dotted with purple and lilac.

'There won't be a reaction until you provide the catalyst. Where were you? On another planet by the look of you.' The class behind giggled. Miss Cameron glanced at them frostily and the laboratory was silent.

'I know that you do not have much interest in chemistry. I know that you are not a budding scientist. I know that you spend most of your time in a world you create for yourself, dreaming away in the art room. That's all very well.'

Miss Cameron was fond of 'that's all very well', especially when it was not.

'That's all very well,' she had told her, 'but you must have an all round education. After this year you need never cross the laboratory door, but until then, until the exam is sat, you are a member of my class. An apprentice of science. It is my job to teach you, and teach you I will. Kindly stop yourself from dreaming, just until the end of the lesson. If you think you can manage it.'

The truth was, Siobhan could not. Once she tried counting how many times she let her concentration wander. Whenever she found herself in the middle of some dream she tried to make notes, she scribbled along the margins of her books or made marks on the back of her hand with a pen. She worked out once that on average it was about three times in every hour, that was once every twenty minutes, not including the times she was asleep. She thought that there were laws of averages, percentages she could have expressed it in. But what she could not understand was what it felt like not to. The absence of dreaming fascinated her. What was it like to be constantly in the present, hearing everything and letting it stick in the mind, straightforward and upright. Ideas that came to her were quickly transformed, acted out in a further development. She did not need television because she had her own inside her head. It supplied her with endless themes and it always included her in the action. It was the controls she lacked. If only she could switch it off for a length of time, as Miss Cameron suggested.

That was why she loved the art lessons; there she could develop manual skills while her dreams played.

'Have you thought of going on with this as a career?'

Siobhan was stunned when her art teacher suggested it. It never occurred to her that a career could be made out of anything other than duty. But her father had been angered when she suggested it. That seemed so long ago. He had been in hospital for a week and it was strange the space he left. He was more noticeable by his absence. She took more care of his silence than she did of his blustery presence, which she used to perfect her act of ignoring him. She pretended to not hear him, to not be moved by him those times. Now, lying in a hospital bed he was smaller, shrunken. Both she and her mother had to strain to hear what he said. When they first went to visit him he had stared then just cried looking from one to the other. It must have been another life-time when he had told her to get something steady in life.

'Learn something proper, not drawing soft pictures. Anyone can do that,' he'd said, indicating with a nod the picture over the fireplace. It was from the Lives of the Saints range. His sister had sent it one Christmas – Saint Anthony of Padua in painting by numbers.

'Like your Aunt Brigid. A good hobby. But you need a proper job, after all this education. I don't mean standing behind a counter all day, that doesn't have to be the way.'

But she had dropped science after 'O' Level. Then she went and upset everyone with her religious vocation. Why didn't she wait for a better time to let them know? Up in the art room everything spun in the girl's memory. There could never be a better time. And now she was not sure about the strength of her commitment.

It was a quiet day. She was finishing a poster for the school dance. She was always asked to produce posters and leaflets for school activities, being good with a pencil. She would create decorative borders and elegant script.

The art room was on the top floor of the middle-school. It was the lightest room in the building on account of the windows which ran down both sides on the longest walls. The ceiling was high, because the room was carved out of the roof. She loved the room. Unfortunately it was also the coldest place in the school. Beneath this room were the third-form classrooms, and down throughout the building with the first-years on the ground level, ranked in order of ascendance, the arts nearest heaven.

The ceiling here was modern and white where the new plasterwork was butted next to the joists. Siobhan thought it looked like a church. Throughout the rest of the school the ceilings were resplendent with the heavy Victorian mouldings for the original lighting. Now narrow strip lights lay between the embossed circles of dusty leaves, which were broken and chipped. The strip lights were ugly, casting a flat, sad light. She used to stare at the mouldings, try to work out how the vines started as the stems twisted round and circled the classrooms.

'Siobhan Doolin! What is so interesting on the ceiling?' And she would return to the book or blackboard.

For this poster she was using the pattern of the mouldings to create a border round the large sheet of cartridge paper. She was locking the stems and weaving them in and out using a black surround and she intended to colour the leaves various tones of sepia like an old print and highlight details with gold paint. The lettering was not black but darkest brown to give the poster a rich look. She was pleased with it as she saw it develop under her hands.

If anyone was looking for her they always knew to try the art room first. Cecile often surprised her there, handing her copies of notes to take to the common room to save her walking all that way.

Siobhan stared out of the window. From her vantage point she could see the park, the frozen lakes, the ducks hobbling across it. One of the worst winters in memory. She loved it. Thick snow and ice transformed the world into somewhere clean and beautiful, but her father could not manage the cold and every day there were reports of elderly people with hypothermia and, on the television, warnings about how to keep warm. Extra clothing allowances were payable that year to pensioners, but that did not stop them from skidding on frosted pavements. They broke hips and knees which did not mend but slowly ached and could not re-knit.

In the park the plants were laid waste. Her father used to talk to gardeners. He was broken-hearted when they told him that the rose garden was destroyed.

'It'll be a miserable display this summer,' he said shaking his head. 'If any survive at all.'

Because he had no garden he always loved plants and open spaces. In the hospital now he had pot plants. Feeling guilty, her mother had taken them in and surrounded his bed with them.

Siobhan enjoyed winter. She liked the smell of the dark nights, liked being indoors knowing that snow fell noiselessly all night. In the morning there were deep drifts and the council sent grit wagons first thing to clear the roads. She had to dig out the front step before going off to school. Siobhan went up to her knees in deep drifts of snow and laughed, but her mother was terrified.

'I'll be buried alive Jesus!' she shrieked as her foot disappeared and Siobhan wanted to laugh, but her mother's arthritis had started to torment her so there was no fun in it.

Winter was the term when Sister Cecile wore black galoshes over her shoes. Some days she forgot to remove them and sat with them throughout their lessons, only noticing when a puddle had formed under her desk.

Siobhan felt her eyes prick suddenly. That morning at assembly it was announced that Cecile had taken ill. Reverend Mother led the school in prayers for her. No details were given. And then the school chaplain put a notice up announcing a mass to be said for the old nun, mid-week.

She remembered Sister Cecile saying that if she could survive November and December she was steady for the year ahead. She always said those two months would be the ones which killed her. But she had got this far, she had to get through now. She just had to. It wasn't fair. Not to go off sick just right now when her father was ill. It seemed to Siobhan that everything was changing, it felt as if there would never be any permanency after this.

A couple of nuns crossed the convent garden muffled against the cold, their black robes severe next to the snow. They walked quickly, carrying baskets.

Some first-years were throwing snowballs over in the far playground, out of sight of the garden. Officially it was forbidden, but as long as the girls did not come to lessons soaking, or cut and bruised by stones buried within the missiles, as long as it was harmless, the staff turned a blind eye to the game. Siobhan watched the gentle tossing of soft white spheres which broke up and shattered as powder.

Someone strode out from chapel, their back towards Siobhan. They took large strides and their arms swung loosely. The back was not broad, not like her father's, the shoulders could have been a woman's. The hair was not so short that it excluded womanhood. It might have been a parent, someone's mother. But the feet were too big, and the walk too masculine. A workman then, or a visitor. They wore a long, dark coat, yet she knew he was no priest, no member of the clergy.

She looked up at the empty sky, opening up for miles, but the sound of giggles and shrieks and feet running made her look quickly down. The first-years had fled and the man was standing still, dusting snow off his coat. He turned around laughing and she saw his face. It was one of the restorers. The younger one, the one that half her class were in love with.

Suddenly the thought struck her sharply, like the snowball must have landed him, that this man had combined both her interests; art and history as a conservator of paintings, an art historian. Why had she not thought of that earlier? Maybe there was something she could do. Suddenly and for no reason the man glanced up, aware perhaps that he was being watched. Siobhan ducked out of the window, blushing. Now he would think that she was another of his admirers. Her cheeks burned and she felt angry, being caught staring.

If only he could have known that. After a while it irritated the man. This strange response from the girls which reduced them to giggling groups that stood around in corridors waiting for him to pass, or hung around outside the chapel door at break. Worse were those who came pretending to pray between lessons and watched him through veiled eyes.

He was not fooled by this sudden interest in himself. It did not flatter him or let him believe he was anything other than he was: a rare male in a girls' school. And he knew what he looked like, he had photographs and every morning the large jaw and busy mouth greeted him in the mirror now that he had begun shaving once more. That was tiresome. At first he had the shock of discovering his face after, how many? Ten years? Was it ten years of beard and concealment?

He had saved up the pieces of his beard to burn, watching them shrivel and hiss after he put them to the match. He breathed their pungent destruction and felt cleansed, a strange ritual, superstitious no doubt to some, full of meaning. He wanted some rite to mark its passing.

The following day he felt naked and visible, he imagined that his chin went everywhere before him and he followed it stupidly. Sometimes, like the frame of his glasses, he became aware of it, could see it below his eyes. He felt as if he was nothing more than a prop, all his body existing as a foil for this part of himself where all acute sensitivity now lodged.

Yet no one noticed. The giggling groups continued to giggle but no louder or more obviously than before. He imagined they laughed because he was clean shaven, he felt his ears warm as he walked past, and a slight blush coloured his white skin. Later he knew that it had been imagined. He did not look different. Even Arturo, whose response he was dreading, did not react.

It was late into the afternoon when he finally asked his colleague if he had noticed anything and Arturo looked blank.

'Noticed what?' he asked.

'My beard?'

'Well I'll be . . . it's gone!' The large man looked perplexed, like a man who discovers his house has been burgled while he slept calmly, to come downstairs and find the silver missing.

'I thought there was something about you but I couldn't work out what. Now I can hardly remember what you looked like with a beard. Isn't it strange?'

And yet Wainsworth felt so different. Lately he thought he might grow it back, just pack up shaving. It was such a bother. He went through disposable razors and shaving soap, then progressed to an electric razor, but he never felt clean, although it was certainly faster.

It felt strange that he had ever had hair sprouting on his face. Something all men were afflicted with. Eager to begin shaving at school, his classmates had vied with each other in the sixth form and grown awful wispy things and been sent home to shave. That was a frightful age to be. He thought that the sixth-form girls in this school were at least dignified. Too cool to hang around him. It was the third- and fourth-years who were the worst. At first he had been embarrassed by the younger girls' mock adulation. Arturo was amused and he envied his colleague's easy manner. But he could not manage that, he felt awkward and preferred the irritating chirpiness of the first-years who milled about him in the yard. They were honest and unashamed, but not him. He inhabited a hidden world of deceit, of seeming innocence. He thought that his work filled all the yearning spaces where his body still ached. Then he realised he was holding himself in check. Until recently he believed he was content. Now he envied Arturo. He even envied his own parents for the type of security they both shared. Age brought a cooling off. Age brought contentment as needs became less prominent.

His hand was rubbing the grains of texture under the paint, softly with the well-practised movement. The saint's gleaming torso lay in front of him, bare as his own might be. Such nakedness was an affront to imagination. He saw instead the pale skin of the dark and silent girl, and his hand was touching that instead as he worked. Soft it would be and he would hold her to him. He was going down into a dream of such pleasure and sweetness that his eyes shut and his hand stopped as if he was a figure in a painting, fixed for all time until some restorer bent a knee this way, turned a hand that, blocked out a tree or erased him.

He straightened up and shook his head, forcing his eyes to recognise the painting and see there the quizzical look of Saint

Polycarp. But for a moment someone else looked silently out at him.

He imagined the judges, hypocrites all, who presided at Polycarp's trial. They followed their instructions. They were to silence this troublemaker for all time. He imagined the stern voice of condemnation and the terrible accusations, 'There's more to you than meets the eye'.

Slander, lies. The saint was innocent. It was he who deserved such shame. When he closed his eyes he saw the eyes supplicating. Images flickered up, out of his control. He squirmed in the presence of his conscience.

He knew that in everyone lurked the capacity for foulness, just as in everyone was the same capacity for goodness. He was paid to spend his hours painstakingly caring for an old painting, so fragile its surface might blow away like dust. Yet he was from a culture which in the past had sent out bands of crusaders to destroy images that did not conform to its own view. And sent out bombers to ruin cities, reducing monuments and treasures to the same grey rubble. A wall painting gone in the time it takes to release a control shaft, crumbling after five centuries. And the bombers had their rules, like knights. They rode out to their deaths in mail, and cooked inside their metal suits.

There was something perverse about him. Whichever way life went he would make it difficult for himself. He started thinking about his ex-girlfriend – he hadn't thought about her for years. Everything used to seem so easy then. Now there were more rules and he could not be free of them.

At break he went out: left the brushes soaking and walked around. December already and the snow crisp under-foot. His breath froze in little wreaths of smoke, wreaths he might lay at his frozen passion, the emotions he kept on ice. Standing in the courtyard he tried to remember how love felt. It was torture, and he was better without it. Love left the scars from sharp razor-edged nights. He filled his life with other things. A sensible man with a career. A sensible man bereft in every way. No spirit, no heart. He needed something or someone to fill that great gap which he let himself peer into for the first time in years. What was wrong with him? He had believed himself happy until that minute. But what was the point in never crying if he also never laughed?

As he stood in the courtyard, a snowball hit him. Squat on his back it thudded. Dry, powdery snow covered his shoulders. It made him laugh and he stooped to scoop up snow forgetting himself for a minute. When he straightened up, the assailants had fled. He glanced upwards still holding his useless missile and saw a face watching from one of the top storey windows.

It ducked out of sight when it was observed. Probably a pupil out of bounds. He wondered how long she had been there? Who watched him secretly, even if for just a few seconds? He had had the impression of dark hair and he felt a sudden agitation when he thought that it might have been the dark and quiet girl he had noticed before. What were those rooms, set away at the top of the building?

He looked for signs of her. He passed her in the corridor silently without a flicker and he saw that she did not perceive him. He thought there was a sadness about her, a silence which made her different from the others. Did she laugh as readily as her friends? He would have stared after her but knew that he would be noticed. Once when nobody was about he watched her as she walked arm in arm with a friend across the courtyard, making her slow way towards a classroom. He had leaned up against the window to see as they passed directly underneath. They went out of sight and he continued his way to chapel without a backward glance.

Last term he had been irritated by Miss Barlock. She had started hanging around, feigning interest in the restoration. He suspected her motive was envy. A frustrated artist, she needed to be seen taking notice of the work. It must have been lousy for her, spending her days getting the younger forms enthusiastic about what they could make out of cardboard and waste paper. The last lot were on display in the hall, everything covered in white powder paint like a perfect Christmas morning. He thought her visits to the chapel were to give her more credibility with the rest of the staff, because it struck him that whatever progress he and Arturo made meant little to her. She would nod and make comments, or worse, ask questions she thought she ought to, and become quite bored with the details. But not everyone could have Cecile's enthusiasm.

It was the old nun who told him that Miss Barlock had been away as a novice once.

'She went off on a sabbatical year, oh, a long time ago now. To see whether she had a religious vocation or not. But she came back to teach, the religious life wasn't for her. She went for a very austere order, not for us. She did not talk about it much, but she must have been very disappointed. She had to face up to what she wanted, not what she thought she wanted any more. You'd never think to look at her that when she first came out of college she was something of a pre-Raphaelite with all this extraordinary long hair let loose. Ah well, we all grow older don't we? We must resign ourselves to what we do.'

He felt that there was a sadness about her, and wished he could feel more sympathetic, but the art teacher irritated him.

Last term she had stopped him in the corridor a few weeks after his disastrous talk to the sixth form. 'I have a good student,' she said, 'and I've suggested that she go for a career in art, but I don't really know all the different avenues. I was wondering . . .'

Wainsworth was always wary of people who said, 'I was wondering'.

'I was wondering whether you might be prepared to talk to her about what you do, fire her imagination a bit . . . let her see some alternatives . . .' she tailed off, seemed to think for a while. 'I wouldn't want to let her think that all she can do is teach. May I send her down to you one day? Only she has been asking me about the correct choice of course for her, if she goes to university or college.'

'What else does she study? She'd need science if she wanted to become a restorer.'

'I think she does a modern language, and then there's history with Sister Cecile.'

'As soon as I get a bit more time I'll be glad to give her some advice,' he said. 'I could have a quick word with her history teacher, just to make sure where her interest lies.' And so he heard her name for the first time, but did not put the name to the face he had been silently watching.

That was last term and he had felt guilty for not arranging something. Wanting to put this right, he went to the common room to find Cecile who surprisingly had not been down to see him after the holiday. At first he did not understand what the sister at the door of the common room meant when she told him that Cecile was not available. Finally it made sense to him. Cecile was ill and a nun's illness is mysterious. The nuns went about their lives behind closed doors. All he ever saw were those who taught, but he knew a troop of them kept house in their closed building. Through doors accidentally left open he had glimpsed once a very old nun and one day another frail sister, carrying a heavy tray up a steep flight of stairs. Now it felt as if a veil had been drawn across Cecile's illness. Whatever it was, it was not to be discussed. He could not discover how ill she was, but when he overheard them offering prayers for her at assembly he began to worry. Now he worked impatiently. That afternoon the saint squirmed under his indifferent hand, which for the rest of the day completely lost its touch.

Cecile lay for over a month, sweating with the virus which made her delirious. Term ended and she did not see Christmas that year but slept throughout the holiday. After three days into the new term the doctor told Reverend Mother that the worst was over.

Cecile opened her eyes and watched the crack of light. Venetian blind stripes of it were beginning to fill the room. Slices of colour and detail that her eye acknowledged. She could not remember the word for the patterns on the ceiling a half circle of leaves and trailing vines. She was sweating. Somewhere in her body something hurt. Her eyes showed reds and orange, brilliant swathes cut through, then black again and now, flickering disturbance.

The bed tilted, her body jarred, as if she had broken her fall. Her heart jumped with fear making her breathing snort loudly. Was that the noise which woke her, ringing in her ears in the soundless space that was her room? Cut into patterns. The vibrating orange and red inside her eyelids. She did not want to see them, and now there was a hard edge of something glassy. No colour, transparent, not white, shining. Silver was a word, blinding another – sharp circle whose centre was invisible of keen light flashing. Eyes dazzled. Back to the red and orange brilliance, the cut of lines, aching on the black space.

'Make it dark,' she muttered, 'make it restful, let me sink away into the softness.'

Her hands were not hands. She felt roots grip her face. Whose face? Where was she?

She reached out to touch it, this thing called face, instead she found a flat surface, continuous going out and on without end. There was no feeling in it. She pulled her finger along the narrow ridge of bone. Once it was a nose, nose for what? For a story? For a song?

Finger then fist sank. Something hollow. Fist turned, kneaded.

Bread it was, dough being thumped on a board. Dough stuck to your fingers and the woman shouted, 'Out of my kitchen!'

At the table, you were up on your toes with just your nose peeping over. Remember, Cecile? It was a flat table and it stretched out for ever in front of your eyes. You might drop off the edge of it and be lost as a boat sails over the edge of the world.

Crash, the dough thunders, massive hands work it. And the room vibrates with pounding. You watch the knife dividing dough into portions. Each portion into a tin, left rising. The loaf is broken. This is my body, the body of my son whom I give to you. This is my blood, the blood of my son which shall be shed for you. Her fingers exploring, a mouth soft open, moist, hard edge of sharp teeth, cutting line, she knows they are neither white nor yellow. They are – what's the word? She has teeth that colour but doesn't know the word. Teeth don't care. They don't understand colour. Teeth understand biting and chewing, those words. She makes a discovery.

The finger goes through, punctures the rising dough and it deflates and the woman shouts at her, a morning's work ruined. And she was such a small child to make so much trouble.

That woman never liked her. Out in the kitchen, the flat table was her kingdom. A common woman with her hair cut short, wearing a thick fringe of hair across her forehead. All the veins on her face broken, rough skinned, her nose broad.

Your mother was white and ill looking. She was a lady.

'Get out of my kitchen!' the common woman said.

'Meddler!' she called you. Meddler. She hated you.

A friend called you moaner.

'Go home moaner!' she said.

The gate swung closed. Massive gate, and it would not open. Outside the wall her friend said 'moaner'. It came over the bricks and she heard it. Heavy, big. A full word. What was it? Over the wall, it found her just as they found her later, curled, crying. She wanted to throw it back. But it was not like that. She could not pick it up. It avoided everything. Ugly thing.

Ears were rough. Sometimes hairy. And leaves. On the ceiling. Smooth, white, fixed. They did not grow. Unnatural. Growing things withered. Dry wrinkled skin.

She was.

Old wood, burnt bread.

'Look what she's made me do now! It's ruined.'

Everything is ruined. A morning's work. The room returned.

The edge of the bed, the wainscot stripe of brown textured with leaves. The world was full of leaves. There had to be something else besides leaves.

A cabinet with a water jar, and the holy water font by the light switch. The cheap utility crucifix. She had always hated it. Plaster moulded from one of those kits. An insult to the figure frozen in death.

Otherwise the room was bare. If she could pull the hanging cord, the stripes would disappear and behind them she would see the wall of the garden.

Of course she could always pray. But who would she pray to? She lay for a long time pondering that question. Her memory could not supply the answer. There had been something once, something she believed in. There was something that did exist, but it was beyond her reason. Reason evaded her. And in flashes she would find herself back inside her childhood. She could not remember what had happened to her once childhood ended, once the sudden bright picture in her mind faded. There was a gap; she was back in the bare room.

At home there were red and gold curtains made of velvet. And in the nursery they were pale lilac, with striped wallpaper the same colour. And she was very light, she could hover in the nursery and watch herself playing. Then she saw her mother gaze up at her.

You were on the ceiling looking down, Cecile. Remember? The ceiling had no end, you went higher and further until you saw that the painted stars were real. They winked and shone and altered like the constellations your father spoke about. The Great Bear, Orion's Belt. You drew them into a book with a mapping pen and your governess was pleased. Next you drew the constellations you saw from the window and Miss Frobisher told you that you had not copied what you saw for there was no such star.

And I had copied it exactly, she cried. One day she would float across to the lawless star.

But belief kept her earthbound, pinned her to the iron bed

of the sick-room. She could see herself lying on it, a long way off. The blankets pressed over the shape of her body, her legs made two ridges of grey shadow on the white coverlet.

She lay without movement. She wanted to reach down and prod her body, touch it, pinch it into shocked life. Make her steady ribcage swell with air. Feel the lungs vibrate. She reached out and everything turned black.

Inside it must be totally dark. A dark which eyes cannot become used to. This is the sightlessness of the end, where nothing exists. The silence of the anchorite's bones wedged inside that shallow space. They held up loose earth. Plants grew, pushed between the outer stones. The tower was a ruined shape, a strange upright coffin. Inside the impression of her body was left in the dark earth. This was peace. When consciousness ceased and she fell into nothing, down through empty space, nothing caught her. Then she would hear a scream and it would wake her, inside the bed, inside the body and she would begin again; wondering whom she ought to pray to, and for what?

BURIAL

ON THE OPPOSITE SIDE of the double monastery, in the monks' section, the man stood upright and wept. His bare feet were cut and bleeding. In the winter he wrapped rags around the soles to keep out the frost, but still they turned numb and he stumbled. Each year was a struggle to survive. In the spring his feet touched damp soil and he rejoiced feeling the thaw. There were not enough skins to put some aside for making sandals. For almost a year he had waited, he would glue old sacks together with the bones he boiled down and he took to wearing the wooden blocks they kept in the kitchen to avoid the chilled tiles in the dorter.

The cold froze his blood, made his bones ache. He walked painfully, unable to rise above his physical prison, unable to fix his mind upon God. Each step became a penance. Only some sandals, yet these things became impossible requests.

Now he buried his head in his hands. When he swallowed he gulped. With each heavy sob he expected to find his raw heart coughed out upon his palms.

When they saw him the brothers stood back or crept away and whispered among themselves. Monks ought not to know such private grief, only collective mourning – Good Friday sadness. Then they might feel misery for the sins of the world, for the sacrifice of God's son. Then might they weep bitterly, but in each tear was the hope of redemption, through death, divine love. But this sorrow which caused their brother to wail was earthly. It was carnal and shocking. They hurried away on soft feet.

Let him beat his breast in agony. What caused him to behave as a father at a child's burial? He was as weak as the Godless, to whom death removes all hope.

His brothers shook their heads and gave no words of comfort. Such sorrow was an embarrassment for it proved that God was not enough.

When he was alone he cared for nothing around him. Once he went about his day dutifully. He did not slack, but would work hard. He knew himself to be only half a monk and if he thought on God a while, he spent the rest of the time thinking on someone else.

He was an able worker and resourceful. He was agile when he joined the order and took pleasure in his health and strength until the last few crippling winters which aged him. The flesh on his hands withered, but he had hope. He believed that his reason to live was close by him and he was a watcher, interpreting whatever he saw to give him reason to keep hoping. The brothers would see how a sudden stillness came over him and they believed he meditated upon God.

He worked in the orchard, climbing the branches with ease, until of late when he wept with frustration as his body ached. He had suffered enough.

'Brother Ferda,' they would say, 'do not be so hard with yourself. A younger brother will perform the hardest of your tasks. You have earned a rest.'

Hypocrite, he called himself. He knew each tree, its character, its strength. Its twisted branches like outstretched hands. He had names for them. Leg-rake, and Thumb-span, and Claw-foot, and for the great spreading brute furthest away he had two names, Scratch-earth or Cut-through. He understood how to speak to them, how to appease and tend each one, for he was skilled in husbandry. All day he worked alone, reading the office from the branches. When they came near they heard him at prayer and left him. But many times he crouched, was still as a breathless corpse and watched from the bough as they searched for him.

The orchard bordered the outlying walls of the monastery. It was part of the track that led towards the forest. On the other side were fields they claimed the tithes from, rented and worked by peasants. Once they had been prosperous, but even as he entered not a score ago, they were faring badly. Winters stripped them of wealth. The fruit trees became barren. Still he sat in their dry branches.

'They will carry again!' he promised and the order believed him because he was skilled.

From the branches he could see occasionally into the other side. Only a scrap of yard and some outhouses, but he had watched among the convent children a tiny thing nursed from infancy and he believed this child was his own. The fruit of his un-Godlike passion. His heart beat wildly the day he first saw her. He had suspected it for long, and happiness warmed him.

Even with her head covered he could identify her by the walk, a slight gait to the left. He watched her change from laughing child to sober girlhood, at last in the white robes of the postulant, a born nun like her mother. He was the false religious of the family.

It had been long before, when he had ridden up to the outskirts of the village, through the wood until the shadow of the monastery fell across the land. They had waited until dark swallowed the shadows before crossing the flat land at a gallop, desperate not to be seen. The horses' sides steamed, their flanks heaved. His travelling companion was big with the child inside her.

He held the horse while she dismounted awkwardly. He held her to him for a moment. The last time. He believed she always knew it was the last time, even as he said he would wait for her in the village. She had not replied. Her eyes were closed, too weary to look at him. But she inclined her head to show that she heard him before trudging towards the woman's side alone.

A storm began to churn the night air. He felt a heavy drop of moisture land on his cheek. He stood watching it build up, until there was rain that drenched all things. He did not move to protect himself, but let the water soak into his undershirt and he remained still, until he knew for sure that she had gained admittance. He waited. Morning came quietly, trembling with apology to the beasts which night had driven to madness. Only then did he turn back towards the village.

For months he had remained there turning his hand at leather work. The tanner had died with the pox two winters before and he was skilled with needle and awl, but he never told them that he learned his skill in a monastery where he would sit among his brothers mending their worn footwear. He thought that he and his beloved could live there, among these simple people, even though she was high born, unused to the ways of men. If they were discovered to be ex-religious they would be driven away. It was better to continue with their original plan.

A full year of waiting and he understood that she had never believed in the plan. She wanted to return to a convent but was too guilty to dream it possible. If, when she entered those walls she rediscovered her true vocation and remained, he could not blame her. He had feared this. Life outside was uncertain.

What else could he do? To be near her he entered as a lay monk. Working, he spent his days in toil rather than prayer, for that he could not pretend. He watched for signs of his beloved. But there were none. Yet at night he swore he heard the sound of a baby, of cries like a mewling kitten, and some nights, torn from his watch, he would listen for the sounds of wailing carried on the silent air, as his mouth moved in empty prayer. Then a story reached the monks' side. The nuns were rearing a baby abandoned by a village woman. The brothers said what a fine thing it was to save one of God's free souls and a sucking goat was killed so milk could be given.

In all that time, never a sight of his beloved, never a mention of her name and he thought then that she had died, the travail too hard, too earthly for her spiritual ways. He sobbed in his cell and at night he listened, certain that it was his child he heard in the screech of hawks, in an owl's grin at the moon.

He waited three years before he saw anything resembling the child. And he was certain this small running thing was his. Long days he spent in solitude in the orchard where he would pretend to read the office daily. Gradually the others believed him to be intent upon a hermetic life and left him. These times he was energetic, the blood moved in him while he felt he was close to his seed, his own blood which ran about on sturdy feet, and he heard laughter from the convent child and listened as it changed to slower, softer sounds. A born nun their daughter. Never to be given back to the world as a worker once weaned and ready, but to be kept among the sisters.

He was heavy with pride, and silent, lest he let slip by some word his sin. For he could not repent it. He could make no atonement. They would send him far away if he confessed, remove him from his last link with his dead love.

That morning news was given that another of their sisters had died. They heard the wooden rattle calling the nuns to pray at the bedside and they for their part added to the prayers.

At table the reader asked them to pray for the soul of Pinnosa the Virgin and at this there was a murmur while they kept their heads bowed. Announcing the death of an elderly brother was more cause for rejoicing, but to be pulled up as abruptly as this sister in God was hard to understand.

None doubted the ways of God. But Ferda stood upright at the table and began to weep, stunned after a lifetime of silence. His only contact torn from him. He called on God but heard no answer. He was demented with grief.

Later that same evening they found him soaked through with sweat. He had sawed up the dead fruit trees, removing their dry branches. He had worked like ten men, driven by anger that God should take the only thing he wanted. That day he blazed with energy. But he did not return for the service and when they went out for him they saw how Cut-through had become Earth-stump, hacked down for firewood.

In the Convent of Fortitude, across the great wall, Gertrude had seen the child fail as she kept vigil in the night. She heard the strange mutterings and tormented cries, the mother of all creation was calling her child back.

Throughout the last days sisters had kept watch so that a never ending stream of prayer was offered up for the soul shortly to enter the Kingdom of Heaven. They understood that this was the end, that this was just a waiting patch, a time to ask forgiveness and prepare the soul, a lull between the living and the dying to let their prayers reach out.

Aelreda remained in her cell for a great many days, sorely troubled. Some suspected that she was in turmoil with her conscience. Now with the extra loss of one of the convent members, the abbess seemed broken. She embarked on a series of private penances.

The day before, Gertrude had raced from the infirmary to seize the heavy wooden rattle which hung upon the stone wall in the cloisters. Planting her feet firmly apart she held the rattle out from her body and began to make a slow circle with it. At first it turned dully upon the wooden roll, and the slats clattered miserably one after the other until she was able to build up speed and spin the heavy object in a fast swirl. Caught inside its own movement the wooden slats whirred noisily, deafening the nun and rousing the rest of the order. Gertrude breathed hard in gasps and her chest began to pound. Never once did her hands slip or the movement slow down, but continued steadily and loud. Her arms ached from lifting the solid piece of equipment but she did not falter. Her eyes closed and she prayed while listening for the first steps of the hurrying nuns.

Towards the low-lying grey stone building they went, fleeting, barefoot so as not to disturb the dying sister. They doused the fire, pulled loaves out of the oven and left all else, rushing to assemble at the bed.

The abbess did not come to the bedside immediately. Some of the older nuns understood, and as they grouped around Pinnosa's bed to pray in unison, these offered up their prayers for Aelreda.

At the sound of the rattle all who could left their work. But there were always some exceptions; Martha was still grinding oats deafly in the mill and none could leave the bedside to bring her over, and the oldest nun in the order had not made it to the infirmary. She had rushed and tripped on the cold cloister floor. She knew that the rattle should be sounding for her, and was too shaken to stand, so she lay spread-eagled on the stone flags and breathed deeply feeling the penetrating chill. Later that day when the nuns set about their tasks for the burial they found her still holding the same position praying for the child's soul.

It was early the next morning that the heavy paschal candle was lit, now mortal life had been extinguished. For the first part of the day, the body would not be touched so that its soul might pass peacefully. No sound was made, but all praying confined to minds, so nothing might disturb the soul's progress. Then a heavy wooden screen was placed before the body of the convent child and Gertrude began her task of washing the remains.

It was a firm young body that bore no traces of suffering, no marks of pain apart from the customary scarring about the shoulders. The child's skin was pale where it was unweathered. Her arms and hands were bitten by the winds and tanned roughly as all others, but her torso was softest white. There were no folds or creases along the belly, no secret stigmata she had concealed. When Gertrude was laying out the older sisters she often discovered the festering sores they never complained about. One sister wore a spiked belt for years under her habit, it made a long putrid wound which oozed. Gertrude had touched it lovingly, for to be base on earth was to be exalted in heaven.

She was used to death's destructive work, of the stink of the corpse in summer. She had seen all the routes to perfection and they were extreme; the nail driven through the thigh to emulate Christ's agony, the cuts in the side, packed out with thorns, grown over and purple. And she saw all bodies, from babes they could not save to the convent children who died during hard winters. Death did not disturb her, but such perfection did.

Three consecutive knocks on the infirmary door brought the robe keeper who waited outside with the white tunic which Pinnosa the Virgin would be buried in. This was handed across the door. None might set foot inside until Gertrude told them that all was as it ought to be.

She took the robe silently and lay it at the foot of the bed. First she wrapped bandle linen tightly around Pinnosa's face, to keep the jaw shut as much as hold the headdress in place. On the eyes she placed weights. When she had dressed the body, she took the tight linen cap and began to fix the head-dress, fastening it in place behind the head with laces. Then the wimple which fitted neatly and close to the neck and the mount for the underveil. She fastened the cream veil carefully with the large pins, careful not to prick the head, although why, she could not understand.

Now it was time to draw back the screen, but before she did, she bent to kiss the girl's cheek. Already the body was cold, beginning to harden. Where she had bent back an arm, a bruise flowered at the wrist as blood gathered under the skin. Her disintegration would be sudden, on account of the harsh way she had treated herself, consuming nothing, living on prayers for the final weeks. Already the body seemed to age. Gertrude would not let them delay the burial, for this child would be returned to her God as she came from him: unblemished, virginal and in his image.

The abbess watched from her cell window as the procession weaved its way across the courtyard to the church.

She snapped her eyes shut as the pallet passed under her window to avoid seeing the white face which lay upon it staring upwards to the sky. She rearranged her veil and pinned the extra layer of black net she kept for further modesty across her face. She went down to join the service, but first crept into the infirmary and stood watching the empty pallet upon which Pinnosa died. Touching the straw she trembled and could not look away as if she saw the young sister still breathing in her illness, an illness and a death agony which the abbess shared, each night in anguish. She would not be able to look upon the corpse of her once daughter in God, just as she had tried to never look upon her throughout her short life.

On the day of the burial it was wet and the sky was dark. That morning the requiem service was sung and on the other side of the grille the monks' voices joined in the refrain, swelling their sorrow upwards for one of their number. But each member of the order felt a special sadness for one so gifted and young to be taken from their midst.

Through the heavy grille the sisters accepted communion across the square cut for the purpose. Each was a disjointed mouth opening in acceptance of the consecrated wafer which, before the priest had blessed them, had been the worthless altar breads that the lay sisters laboured to make on the enormous metal bread press, kept smooth with wax from the guttering candles.

Six nuns lifted the pallet and carried it through the cloisters. Followed in procession, they went past the outhouses, through the gardens towards the little walled cemetery where the freshly dug grave waited to accept the body. The monks' voices floated out from the church after the burial procession, all that they could send towards the woman's side. Gertrude swung the incensor and the small gate opened to allow them in.

The body of the child was lifted from the pallet and laid across six bands of linen which were wound tightly around the hands of the supporting nuns. The crucifix placed across her was removed and dropped first into the grave, they heard it splash in the rain water which had collected since yesterday. As the oldest nun came forward to read the prayers, the sisters began to lower the body in stages. Eight jerking movements in all, as they unwound the linen straps.

The abbess felt her veil blow over her head where it flapped like a bird with broken wings, unable to soar. She wanted to be a long way off, watching from a distance. She dreaded this intimacy of burial, feared her reactions. Rain pelted. It turned the open grave to mud. Pinnosa's body touched the bottom and they heard a splash. The abbess clutched her chest. How terrible it was to be laid in a dirty puddle of water. Already mud was soaking up the robes, the white headdress was stained and parts of the child's face were underwater. The dirt left grey traces on her alabaster skin.

Aelreda stepped forward, to see her child for the last time. But the sight was worse than she imagined. Death should be beautiful and she wailed with a cry that was ageless. The noise of all life-bringers contemplating death. Death should be shining. That was what she had been promised. Not this foul mortal burial. And Pinnosa would be left alone with stinking water and wormy earth surrounding her.

Two nuns began to shovel clay back onto the grave. The pale face was covered in scattered patches of red earth. The soil was very rich here. The cemetery smelt. Death was anything but sweet. It was foul; corruption in its worst form. Decay. The end to which all things came. Behind the abbess the nuns were kneeling, but she did not notice.

'Domine Misere Super peccatrice.' As she heard the words Aelreda quickly began to kneel but as she bent her knees, all strength went from her legs and she felt herself being caught by several pairs of hands. In the procession back to the choir stalls, Aelreda leaned against a sister. She took her place shakily, and sat while the rest of the order knelt, to spend what was left of the day in prayer for the repose of the soul of Pinnosa the Virgin.

There was nothing of the monk Ferda. He tore his habit, covered his head in ashes and wandered as a penitent, his watching finished. The monastery could not hold him. He no longer cared whether he lived or died and gave in to despair. He was seen in many villages, written about as he passed through communities bringing chill winds and the sweating sickness with him. In some places they closed their gates and would not allow him entrance. Horsemen passed him in the forest and rode fast to spread the news in settlement and town, for his grey, malingering presence and terrible sorrow were dreaded.

The Convent of Fortitude. The Year of Our Lord's Grace 928.

After the time of the three deaths our abbess Aelreda was as a lost soul. They said what caused her to suffer was God's taking of the best of the novices. Her skill cannot easily be replaced and our abbess's plans for a great library were snuffed out like a candle, as was her spirit. For a long time she went among us as if a light had gone from her.

And Werberga is ailing. She is forced to entrust to my care the newest pupils, but I lack skill to train them well. Nowhere is the shout of creation, instead we are an echo to a once greater sound. Werberga might grip a pen but her hands cannot move as her mind dictates.

The time now comes to re-elect our abbess. We must be ready to replace Aelreda who can no longer see to practical matters.

In my postulancy always my eyes were bent over my book. A slow dawdling student, I had no time to see around me, but in my life I hope to see the great scriptorium once spoken of, established here.

Werberga places a silence over the time when she was acting abbess. And if I knew all that passed still I could not commit it to letters lacking the skill of my mentor.

Werberga when she finishes her last great work tells me that she will commend her soul to God. And in her absence I must continue, yet I fear her going from us.

*I pray that it will not be a time of famine, of starved souls
without hope. Lord, look favourably on us your servants and let
strength grow in our midst.*

23

RECOVERY

'AND PRAY FOR SEAMUS Doolin,' the priest ended the list of special intentions.

The woman and her daughter, who had both come in late, looked down as if they had been given a cue like actors waiting in the wings, tense and ready to pounce into the lights. Anyone standing behind them would have seen the backs of their necks as they bent their heads simultaneously to the name of Seamus Doolin. Anyone standing behind them might have noticed the girl's sudden flush of colour which reddened even the tips of her ears.

The girl's mother secretly wished that they suffered the normal rows at home, those ones she read about in the problem pages of magazines. 'Dear Anxious of the Midlands, You must let your daughter know that you will not continue to let her treat your home as a hotel. Try taking a firm stand.' Those were the usual tribulations of having a teenage daughter.

She would have preferred a row over the earrings, and a compromise: 'Get them done but no long dangly things, and only at weekends.' But the girl wasn't bothered and now it was this business of wanting to leave home, not like the reasons on the letter pages. And heavens knows they were bad enough. But no, her daughter had to be different.

Why couldn't she be like any normal teenager with bloody normal concerns? Why did she have to be so odd? This business of becoming a nun – who could she talk to about it? There was no one in the family before who'd been a church person. It wasn't an honour to her way of thinking; it was freakish, unnatural.

They all went to mass and she knew what she believed in, although she couldn't have told anyone why, but to want to enter an order! That was taking things too far.

For the first time ever, she started suggesting things her daughter might do when she left school; asked if there was anything she could do to help. She even praised her, showed an interest in how she did in her exams. She wished she hadn't been so resentful about her staying on, and regretted that she had ever made it difficult. No, let her be a sodding career girl if that's what she wants – anything rather than join a convent. She wanted the possibility of grandchildren, or another generation. The closest anyone got to immortality.

Maybe the shock of the past few weeks would knock it out of her. What an outburst she'd had, God forgive her. And after, Siobhan cried and cried, she could hear her through the bedroom walls. But her daughter must have known that she always yelled things when she was angry. When she tried to explain why she'd said it, Siobhan hadn't believed her.

'Do you think I'm stupid or something?' the girl said. 'You tell my father I'm not his child, he drops out of shock, and now you tell me you were only being funny.'

The girl had been furious with her, or worse, disgusted. It seemed that she would have accepted any version of the lie, only she would not let her get away with pretending it was only intended as a joke. No, she'd rather believe her mother intended it as a malicious lie, or worse take it as the truth.

'All right then,' she shouted. 'He's not your father. Now are you satisfied?'

But the girl wasn't. What kind of slut did her daughter think she was?

Siobhan was cutting herself adrift from them – from their arguments, from their life, and she had helped her.

Yet even Siobhan would have to admit that with him out of

the way, both of them had been calmer, happier in a strange way.

Nothing was said, but they resumed as normal a life as they had ever had. They had even laughed like conspirators when she said that she'd lost her temper and wanted to shock him into silence. 'I went a bit far didn't I?' They laughed until tears streamed down their faces, until their sides hurt and they could not get their breath. It was a sort of fit. They were out of control. Then there had been a silence. Siobhan had said that she shouldn't feel so bad about it.

'He was winding himself up for it Mum. You just gave him a push.'

As the priest left the altar they stood up. The woman was aware that she had not heard a word of the service, except when the priest had mentioned her husband's name. Everything else had passed her by. She bit her lower lip and watched the altar boys glide into the sacristy.

Outside church it was dull and windy. Siobhan pulled her beret as far down as it would go to cover both ears. Mrs Doolin shivered. She fiddled with her gloves as they waited to buy the *Universe*, but wanted to get away before anyone spoke to them. She noticed that Siobhan winced as Mrs Cormack came towards them.

'So sorry about Seamus. It can happen to anyone. But what can you do with these men? They work themselves to death, some of them.' She rolled her eyes heavenwards.

'When do you expect him home?'

'Well if he keeps going as he is, they say he'll be out for New Year. He needs plenty of rest.'

'Well he's in the best hands,' the large woman said touching her gently on the arm.

'You'll see to it he doesn't work too hard now won't you?'
She nodded.

'He'll have to take it easy when he comes out. Tell him I was asking for him.' Then turning to Siobhan, 'We're all praying for your father,' she said. 'God bless you dear.'

They watched her bulky figure as it crossed the street. All the neighbours were praying. Why not? What they saw was his public face, his charming, polished self. They were the ones who had to live with him. Like the neighbours they prayed. The woman prayed they would send him away convalescing. She dreaded the idea of him at home all day, invalided out of work. She had no idea what Siobhan prayed for, but hoped it wasn't a vocation.

Mrs Cormack waved from across the road before she turned a corner and vanished.

'We'd better get home, I've got washing on the line. I forgot to bring it in last night.'

Any excuse to hurry, yet both knew it was crazy to think of routine when he was ill.

Secretly, Siobhan wished that what her mother had yelled was true. To have an uncertainty about the man she called 'father' was something she would enjoy. Of course she did not tell this to her mother.

It could be true. She reasoned it out. There was no problem with birth certificates because her mother had been married to him when she was born, so he would be named as her father even if she was another man's child.

She read up how in the Middle Ages illegitimacy was a matter of inheritance. Well she had nothing to inherit. An illegitimate person was not officially supposed to attain high position in society, or in the church. Was she the new round then, the one whom no one expected to attain anything.

She didn't want to teach or do nursing as was expected now that she had remained at school. Her mother asked her what else there was.

'You don't want to be stuck in a shop, or a factory, you've got qualifications, and by this time next summer you'll have more. You ought to use them. That's what your teacher said. She's still ill isn't she, Sister Cecile? Will she be back next term?'

But Siobhan was stuck for an answer.

'I was thinking that I'd like to study history. I would have asked Sister Cecile about it last term, but with her being so ill . . .'

'But after? What would you do after? All there is is teaching isn't there?'

'There's research,' Siobhan said, but in fact she did not know.

'What about museums?' her mother suddenly said. 'Wouldn't you need history to work in one of them? That's a point, who labels all those exhibits, you know, puts things in glass cases and decides what we'll see?'

For the first time that she could remember, it seemed as if her mother was offering to stand behind her.

'Listen,' she told her. 'You just make sure you have a better life than I did. That's all. Don't end up like me and your dad, although if anything were to happen, I'd miss him. Probably even the rows. At least we're never bored, are we?'

That morning the newspaper man who served her mother commented that she looked sullen. He must have thought she was deaf the way he spoke about her.

'Teenagers,' he said, rolling his eyes. 'I've had enough trouble with my own.'

Usually her mother would agree, enter into a litany of complaints over the Catholic papers. But this Sunday she was silent, handing him the money and taking the *Universe* under her arm in a tight roll.

'God knows it's not been easy for them,' Siobhan heard someone say as they walked off.

'Nothing's ever easy for anyone,' he grumbled.

Yet Siobhan thought her mother looked more relaxed, while she was aware of behaving in a more guarded manner than usual. She did not want anyone to know how easy she was finding this difficult time.

On the first day back at school in January Siobhan went to the library and read up about university courses. Sister Cecile was still not back in class. Siobhan knew that she was having a change of heart, she doubted that she wanted a religious life.

Her faith wasn't shaken, just her desire to serve God in such a way. There was a whole world out there and lots of ways of serving Him. She worried how the nun might react on hearing it. There was no one she could own up to apart from Cecile. And besides, it was ironic but her mother was definitely being more encouraging. Was her mother coming round to the idea of a daughter in a convent now that she was changing her mind about it?

24

FAITH

THERE WAS A STILLNESS about the convent and a silence. That was what struck Cecile as she was allowed up to take a few faltering steps. Her first walk from the edge of the bed to the window-sill proved her weakness. It was a shock, as was the room which was unfamiliar and scrubbed, and she did not know why she had been taken there when she woke in it one morning. She thought she had passed a single night with strange disturbed dreams, but Sister Anselm told her they had had the doctor in twice, and she had been isolated from the other sick. The infirmary was usually empty, due to the nuns' stoic acceptance of ill health. She was in a bare room at the end of the longer one which could accommodate five sisters. Only one of the beds was occupied by Sister Aquinas the oldest nun in the convent, who since the previous winter had become a permanent resident. Every day they waited for news of her death. Cecile did not know it then, but there were those who thought she might go first.

Now she held on to the metal rails at the foot of the bed. Her scrawny hand pressed the white knob. The bed took her weight, she balanced and the frame supported her. She could not let go. The smooth white sphere pressed itself into her palm.

She was exhausted, perspiration dotted her upper lip and her head felt light yet she hung on, forced herself to remain in that position until she could bear it no longer. She slumped

back, crawled to get between the covers before Sister Anselm
caught her.

She could not pretend that she was all right. Even that
small effort left her shuddering, crying with burning sickness.
Sister Anselm told her she had lain for over a month. Cecile
was shocked.

'You did a lot of shouting early on, the first ten days
were the worst, mostly at night. The dark seemed to aggravate
you.'

Cecile wanted to know what she had said. The infirmarian
told her it had been meaningless.

'I would bathe your head with a cold compress and say
your name. Sometimes you spoke about your mother, or your
family, but believe me it was indecipherable. I'd just agree with
anything you said. But most of the time you weren't aware of
anyone.'

Cecile recovered slowly. It annoyed her. Her body was loath
to repair itself. Each day she attempted to walk; she progressed
and could get as far as the window. Those few steps were such
an achievement. Later she would try to remember the euphoria
at being able to manage such a small thing, but this time she
really was the prisoner of her body.

Illness makes you depressed. Life appears faded and worn
as the night shirts you wear which are taken each day to be
disinfected and smell of harsh, uncomforting scents.

All was stark. Her body had been denied excess. There
was just enough of everything. The room was furnished, yes:
a bed and a chair. You could assume two attitudes. But there
was nothing else, except the crucifix on the wall. No table or
cupboard to keep anything in, not that you had anything, not
even a prayer book.

Empty, empty, she looked around her. The world was empty.

When she could get as far as the window the chair was
moved and Sister Anselm helped her into it. Then she watched
the convent grounds.

A brick wall ran down one side. Behind this was a bare

tree. That wall felt like her life. Solid. Day after day it was either pelted by rain which wet its bricks to a shiny gloss or baked by the winter sun into a chalky top dust. She hated it. It stopped her view. Only let her see the top half of the tree. Its roots were pushing themselves under the wall. For years they must have grown silently, waiting to emerge in daylight. The wall had a bow in it. She had never noticed it. One day, that tree would push the wall apart. The idea made her happy. When she put her hand to her face she was surprised to find tears.

She was disturbed that she had spoken about her family. She remembered dreams where her mother accused her of never having a vocation. What had she wanted when she joined the convent? Was her mother correct?

She was a stranger to herself. Nothing was certain. She had rows in her dreams. At home they did not argue, no one raised their voice. She had returned there, stood on the same floor and shouted, as she ought to have many years before. Returning she let her father know how angry she was, let him know that because of him she would be a decent woman. A terrible burden he bequeathed them. She too had wanted ecstasy. She got convention.

'I wanted to be respectable.' She woke up one morning and heard the last sentence from her sleep.

Decency? Was that her reason for coming here all those years ago? Did her mother understand more than she said?

The tree was bare. When would the tiny new leaves sprout? She did not care if they ever did. She had no enthusiasm for new life. What would become of her if her health did nothing to improve? But was this state much different from her usual one? Yes, before she had had her work, her reason to live each day; now the days were stark. They stretched ahead of her and glared, challenging her to fill them. Hungry, pitiful days and she was without energy; she was the last, tired entry on the frayed school report that was carried home each summer: 'lacks motivation'. That was her, the bottom line on a dull list.

But for the rest. Was she happy as a bride of Christ? Had that been enough?

She stood up from the chair and looked down at the dark floor boards. Her feet were a long way off, a telescope turned the wrong way. Had she grown during her illness? Nothing would have surprised her. She did not recognise her body. It was hollow. She felt light and grabbed the chair to stop herself rising to the ceiling. Then the room vanished; dissolved around her, she was left in empty space.

She recovered slowly: had no idea how ill she had been. The school said masses for her. They offered prayers each day and Siobhan lit a candle for her teacher every Sunday. Even the two restorers were caught up, they worked with a type of fury, wanting to be able to finish the panel in time to show it to the old nun, in case she did not last.

Reverend Mother shook her head sadly when Wainsworth inquired after her health. Father Armitage walked slowly along the aisle as the nuns rose, his face grave. A special mass for Cecile. Wainsworth asked everyone.

'But what is wrong with her?'

Reverend Mother was unable to give a clear answer.

'Some type of fever. A combination of things have brought it on. The weather, you know, always unsettles her, and last term was particularly bad. Her bronchitis flares up each time. Then she is greatly weakened; but you have seen how she drives herself, she will not allow herself to rest. Even when ordered.'

Reverend Mother's lips were drawn tightly in indignation.

'It was my responsibility to see that this did not happen. I gave her too much time away from communal discipline, and she has overworked herself. She forgets to eat, then cannot. And so her body is always secondary, but not to God, to her mind.' Her hands gripped both her elbows angrily and Wainsworth understood. Cecile's religion was history. Reverend Mother was shaking her head.

'She's still ill. Her age does not make it easy.'

Wainsworth felt lethargic. Without the old nun, the panel

could not excite him, without her it lost part of its meaning.

When it was given out at assembly that Sister Cecile was recovering an audible sigh of relief went round. But Cecile could not be rushed. Alone in the sick room she spent days remembering. Sometimes a word came into her mind and she took all morning to understand it. Thoughts came and went without control. Her father lived out his lie every day, a respectable man. Possibly he wanted to save them pain.

Her religious vocation was her way of refusing those values she had been taught to honour; family, marriage, children. It was her rebellion, a mark of defiance. She had thought it was her father's action that had prompted her, pushed her into a greater decency, but she began to realise that decency had nothing to do with it. It was a vindictive action to strike her mother. A desperate plunge into a world where she might experience joy.

The carnal terrified her. She had no knowledge of how it worked. Descriptions were shattering and incomplete. As an educator she had to put her ignorance to rights, she was expected to give the girls guidance. She read in an open-minded fashion all the literature the convent possessed. The teaching staff discussed how to treat delicate issues. There were new ideas, fresher approaches, and they had to keep up if they were to be able to assist the girls. The nuns were not ashamed to call anything by the proper name, they kept their minds open and their bodies shut.

It was the reality which Cecile dreaded. The impossible. An awful, ghastly action. When she thought of it in non-teaching language, it made her nauseous.

Was that what her father had wanted? What was the power of it to make him risk his family? Such power to make men and women slaves to each other.

Who needs noble ideals? Forget your noble ideals. Start living. That's why you chose the convent. Because then the pain from your family couldn't hurt you. But pain magnifies in silence, doubles like a cancer cell. And all around is empty space, except for the echo of a scream.

When at last Siobhan saw Cecile she was shaken by how different she looked. There was no general vitality about the nun. At times she would seem possessed by a sort of desperation. Then the old nun would glance around to see if anyone else watched her. It made Siobhan uneasy. Cecile kept beckoning her closer, then would stare at her and shrink back into the chair. Sister Anselm crept away and Siobhan did not know whether to sit on the bed or kneel, so she remained awkwardly by the one chair in which Cecile sat looking absently out of the window.

Cecile had always had such fervency, such energy, that it was terrible for Siobhan to watch her slipping away into her own thoughts, forgetting that she was there. The girl wondered if this was what a life devoted to Christ had brought her to. She did not know whether she had the strength to devote her life to Christ any more if it meant the exclusion of all else. Sister Cecile once told her that the discipline exerted by the order had prevented her from studying. Was that the sort of sacrifice she could make? She was inspired by Cecile's example, she thought to live a good life. But she wanted greater satisfaction for it. She wanted what the order called 'personal ambition'.

Suddenly Cecile's face changed. She was saying something, but the words were indistinct. She was no longer impassive. She beckoned. Siobhan leaned towards her. There was a flicker. Her eyes opened wide then shut tightly. And the old nun sat back without further movement. Siobhan thought she had misheard. Cecile's words had been whispered. Her voice was low. Did she tell her to stop? Or was it what she wanted to hear, did she imagine the nun's words telling her to change direction while there was still time, she could not be sure. She thought she said 'get out' and she wondered if she meant that she ought to go, but Cecile had kept on talking, had said something about ruining her life. Whose life?

Don't let them have it, don't sacrifice it for something
. . . to find that it is no longer there.

That was what she thought she heard. The old nun fell back,
exhausted and silent and Siobhan crept out of the room softly,
so nothing might disturb the other nuns who waited outside.

PART SIX

FADING

25

COLD

THE OLDEST SCRIBE SAT in her cell. The scriptorium had not been in use for many months, it was leaking and they were unable to repair the roof. In the cold the pigment separated in the horns and the remaining gold leaf was too solid to use. The quills had no spring in them and pithy ink clung to the points. Candles were running out. There was no tallow left for dipping and no wax in the comb – the bees were asleep.

She was hungry. That gnawing feeling in her belly was constant. They pulled up ferns; from the roots they made bread, sometimes a type of porridge. They heard that in places men stripped the bark from trees and ate it. They still had laying hens, four goats and some sheep. What corn they retrieved had been smoked over fires and ground into fine meal. The bread made from it tasted sweet like malt.

They had exchanged the last book they could, but who wanted books while their bellies ached? No merchant or lord would give them anything. What remained of their library was without value. Parchment could not feed a starving province. These were times when a man might sell his children for a piece of bread.

But the scribe decided which work could be undertaken for the glory of God. She believed in the dignity of effort. That had been instilled into her as a novice by Elgiva, a tireless instructor who trained under the celebrated Werberga, whose skill was legendary. Under her tutelage many others were set alight, who caught the sparks from Werberga's soul and blazed briefly, embers from her greatness. Then there had been such a glow.

They retained a small *Lives of the Saints* which Werberga had copied and she remembered another wonderful book they had once possessed, which was also her work. It was a book of learning, an encyclopedia of the natural world where in columns Werberga named every living thing, every plant, with beautiful illuminations and a description. The book was decorated throughout in all manner of devices and on each page was a subject to study. All the learning of this world was in that book and she had bent long over those pages, studying not only the matter but the skill with which it was constructed.

But the abbot made them give this up, saying it was a book of little worth without tales of miracles or of Jesus' suffering. And so they offered it to a master mason who wanted satisfaction of a debt, long owing to his father and made such threats and oaths, the monks were all fearful. She wondered if he might try to barter it: well let him see who would give him grain, let him see how it might save him now when all bellies were empty.

Elgiva told her pupils that a second book had been planned, which would contain matters medical, knowledge of the anatomy, humours and physic. But this was not completed and the part manuscript was lost. It was a blow to the school, for pupils came from all the houses to be trained as scribes. She arrived, the unmarriageable daughter that her father thought might do some good in a convent. So the order sent her to Fortitude, where she might learn their careful script. And she progressed to the work of illuminating, following the designs of her predecessors.

'Werberga took on more work than a lifetime could allow,' Elgiva told her. The renowned scribe was dead before the first complete set of illuminations was bound together. All that remained was the small *Lives of the Saints*, but she studied the curved letters, the fast running hand Werberga was so skilled with. Compared to it, her own work was solid, upright. She had not such ease in the execution of her work; her hand would tremble like a novice when asked to ink inside an outline, or use the free brush. Even now she knew her figures lacked the vitality of her teacher's.

None had matched Werberga who excelled in initials. She left behind her interlacing, narrow ribbons so fine that in the space of a thumb's width she counted upwards of one hundred crossings of white lines edged with brown. And spirals, coiled one within the other meeting at the centre of the circle, their tails twisting into endless patterns. In a lifetime she could never acquire such skill. But she was a good worker who made much of the routine work.

She had learned to file gold carefully and rub it with sour vinegar until it blackened. She knew the right amounts of salt to add, or bullock's gall. When the novices had difficulty she would show them how to fix the gilding by pasting the white of egg, and she showed them how to purify their pens each time in salt and vinegar.

Good practices she had, but these did not make her great. Yet she was particular, always selecting the bladders for size, and boiling her own fish heads. She did not believe this was the work of lay sisters or convent children. She took pride in her preparation, and her black ink was much sought after by other monasteries. For this she always cut the wood in spring, just before life burst in the branches when the bark was sweet with sap. This gave the best residue when left to soak and she knew never to rush the small parchment bags as they hung to dry. This was the nigrum optimum ex carbone and she would only let it be tempered with wine. They came to her for yellow carum and hot sangui draconis. She had recipes for folium and good green, and made a fine but grainy smalt for outlining. In all this she was confident, but alongside Elgiva's work her lettering was plain. She could interlock, but it was a laboured work from her brush, not inspired.

In the *Lives of the Saints* a prophet speaks, and the messenger crouches back appalled. The curve of his terrified body bends into the frame. The crooked finger of the prophet sends out a line against which the messenger's protest is useless and his mouth opens in a simple black circle, an endless complaint. And animals wear rolls of muscle, to match the flowing patterns of the draperies which fall as pleats across the saints. But despite such magnificent work, the sisters' influence waned. They became trainers rather than creators. They were to copy and put into writing the thoughts of great men. Gradually the spark of learning they once kindled was allowed to die and other monasteries became the centres for debate and study.

In other places the rule which they so faithfully observed was redefined and expressed. In other buildings it was being adapted into a new expression. A joyous loving brotherhood which valued friendship amongst men and taught how souls shackled to bodies must rise above them but they, prisoners to their wombs and foul female nature, could never rise.

The scribe shivered. She could not remain in her frozen cell. She must join the others. She took up her frame on which the taut piece of skin was stretched and waiting. In her other hand she carried the ink horn, and made her way unsteadily to the kitchen. This was where they crammed to study and work, conserving heat by breathing together, using the warmth from the ovens if there was anything to bake.

She was grey and ill. Her fingers were purple edged as she stumbled through the deathly corridors towards the belly of the convent. Each nun had a sack and a bale of hay. They were depleted in numbers so the convent buildings seemed too large for them, as they adapted to huddling in one cramped space.

Bad-temperedly, because she liked her solitude, she took up a place in front of the one candle with its large disc of metal to reflect the light. She settled and started working, listening to the voice of the reader who spoke the lesson.

None of them could venture to the chapel to sing vespers or lauds, in case the terrible rains began again and they would be stranded. They performed what religious duties they could in the confined kitchen.

They sustained themselves. For a while they had flesh meat after two sheep were drowned, but now those supplies were exhausted and they pulled up roots, searched for insects, or whatever they might live off.

She waited for the knot in her stomach to lessen. Eventually it would slip away. Then hunger would cease to be a problem. She prayed that she might also forget the cold. If she could just stop feeling.

Outside, when it rained again, it fell as freezing hail. The man took up his bundle which he had tied securely to a rod. He slung this across his shoulders. He seemed resigned, there was no other way. Behind him his wife copied, almost as if he had given a signal. She picked up a similar sized bundle, bound in rags and fastened it around her shoulder taking no more notice of it than the man did of his. She sighed heavily. The bundle twitched. She had wrapped a winding sheet around it so that the newborn thing was hidden from view. It was only a matter of time before it died. Then it would be at peace, and the weight she carried lighter.

In the dark hovel there were movements; three other children, two so small they could barely walk and another, older, but leaning awkwardly against the man as in solemn procession they left the ruined shelter that once had been the home of a peasant, a tiller of the rotten earth.

They had seen it from a distance. One wall had collapsed, but the three remaining looked sound enough to keep the wind from their backs, and they trudged toward it, their feet sinking in clay. The floors had sunk under the deluge, but they had lain against the furthest wall and slept, waking to feel more rain on their faces through the open rafters. But they must keep moving. The children's breath was so light they thought they might not wake and he would begin to dig weakly with his hands to prepare some type of grave. He had not the strength to make the pit decent. Then there would be movement and his hands would stop, his energy spent uselessly. And he was angry. The woman did not cry. She did not speak, nor seem to notice anything, but moved like a slow, dull beast unable to endure further pain.

His face was leathery. He was broad-footed. A free man who came under no protection from lord or church. He did not speak, but communicated his intention to continue their walk just by a look. He had made a decision and, awful as it was, there was nothing to change it. He said nothing, but she understood.

They would continue until they reached the monastery, but they would not ask the nuns for alms. That was shameful and besides it was a useless ploy, no one had charity to give these days, and they were not beggars. Once the man had been proud of his wife's robust condition. A couple of strong workers they had been. He could harness a plough and drive as straight as any man and on hiring days never left the fair without his hand taken and his tool sack exchanged.

While there was strength left in them they had their labour to sell, even if their bodies had become weakened. From sunrise till long after it set they were accustomed to work. Now all they wanted was a bellyful of food and somewhere to sleep in payment. They would present themselves to the monastery and ask to be taken on as lay workers. The convent would take her in and he would go to the monks' side. He knew they would not take the children, except possibly the eldest boy if the monks could make use of him. They must abandon the others. He prayed the baby would be dead before they reached the gates.

They approached at last in death-like silence. They went first to the women's side. He would wait until he saw her go inside, restrain the children from running after their mother. Then he might beat them soundly and leave them so weak they would not know what had happened, and he would pray that their time of suffering be short.

At the turn-gate they stopped and the woman touched the stone wall with her fingertips. Now she understood what she must do to survive. It was final. She swooned. He saw her fall. She caught the bell rope as she went down. It rang hopelessly. He listened. There was no sound from within, just like the last place they had gone to, a chapel with its clergy dead inside and no one to unbolt the doors, the church lands empty. The only people who passed them on the road were freemen like himself, the lost who wandered from place to place, who stared ahead and walked towards something on the horizon which no one else could see.

Now they had come so far, he would not believe it was in vain. With his last scrap of energy he threw himself against the silent turn-gate and beat it with his fists while his children played weakly with the bell rope, seeing who had strength enough to make it ring, finding harmless amusement in this and with it a final terrifying energy.

In the kitchen the scribe began outlining with red madder the bodies of the deer and stag. Around the capital they stood proudly, their heads interlocking and their tails split and re-joined. She elongated the tongues and wove them back in circulets into the other beast so that its neck appeared to bend and grow from it and the animals were circular without beginning or end. Her concentration was complete. The cold hours sped.

She heard the lonely bell ringing, but there was nothing they could give. At intervals it rang throughout the night as more unfortunates tried.

In blue she filled in part of the body, then on to this she traced the red criss cross pattern which changed to purple as the colours merged. Her candle was guttering; someone had moved another into her corner. She had not noticed. Everyone slept, or prayed silently. She continued to work. The dark hours were almost over. She laid the quill down, spat on the remains of the one candle and, drawing the sack about her, slept for a while. She heard the bell throughout the remaining night.

In first light the page showed leaping animals, their bodies twisting in mid-air. They seemed to hang. It was the same light which fell upon the family, their legs and arms wrapped around each other in a solid web of limbs, clinging as they pressed against the turn-gate.

It was the gate keeper who realised something was stuck. She took out their refuse at dawn. Now they dumped it outside so that they might avoid contagion. Recently scavengers came from the ruined village. She would hear them shouting and yelling as they fought each other. It horrified her; the coarse words and dreadful scrabble of feet, the thuds and moans, pitiful on the starved air.

This morning there was silence. Only the scream of birds circling and she wondered why no one came. She started to crank the heavy handle. The chain rotated, pulling the big wheel and the gate began to move. She emptied the sacks into the open slats then continued turning the handle, but the gate stopped half way. Something was blocking it. She turned it back a quarter, then set the wheel loose so it might gather speed and swing round past the obstruction. She put her weight against it and pushed, but it was wedged. She peered through the open slats and saw a twisted mass of brown and earthen sacks. What it was she could not make out until she saw hands. She screamed as the upturned face of a corpse came into view. An expanse of pale forehead with sightless eyes rolled back. Part of a group, the bodies wrapped around each other. Then she saw a small hand like a fragment of stonework, the lost piece of a statue. A child's hand held inside a larger.

While it was still morning, lay sisters pulled them apart and dug a narrow pit outside the walls.

The Sisters of Polycarp The Martyr.
The Year of Our Reckoning, 993 by the Grace of God.

Your wrath was great. You threw down churches. Trees were torn up by the roots. The world shook with your anger. Men covered their ears and tried to flee but from the high places even the great fell.

Eaves broke in two, snapping like old fishbones and the earth's plate tilted and sent men rolling to the edges of the land, out into the oceans and beyond.

And the sky those days was false, showing three moons.

Men knew not what to do but thought the judgment was on each one. Great was our sorrow to be alive. We prayed that you take us to your bosom.

The great timbers of the scriptorium collapsed and crushed desks beneath. Pages tore from all the books left open upon stands, and a roundel of the four Evangelists which was stretched in place, you did cleave in half with a heavy shaft of wood.

Such was our misery and confusion at your displeasure.

Our monastery you cracked as an egg that a good wife breaks against a bowl. Our bell tower crumbled.

The turn-gate and outer wall came down, and all around us great stones fell.

We fled, taking to flat land without trees, where we prayed as the world broke up.

These are times when no society is left unharmed. Bands of wanderers go from one place to the next, monk and labourer alike.

We arrived in the plain, myself and nine of my sisters whom you have spared to continue your work, and desist from all works profane.

And I have grown old here, waiting to return.

We kept but one book and a psalter. A man travelling through took them in exchange for a relic he carried with him. A piece of the shin bone of Saint Polycarp. Another, once a monk of Jerome, made us a trunk and painted on the side of it this saint.

We asked him to make an image of our monastery as it was, and from our descriptions he has painted it in behind the saint, with the tower as we told him it appeared.

The oldest of us here, once a teacher in the order, recalls a story of a holy woman skilled in medicine, who was imprisoned. This is why the tower stands she says, to remember her. But she is old and thinks to talk of Saint Barbara whose wicked father locked her away. She remembers from the small Lives of the Saints *but forgets the sequence now her memory is feeble.*

Around the three unpainted sides of this trunk we will add the names of patrons as we raise from the dust a new foundation.

To our dead brothers and sisters, this new order shall be dedicated. And in this we are in obedience to our brothers following the correct rule of nature. For man should go before woman, as Christ went before his mother, who alone of all women is pure.

In time, a new altar will be raised on this site. It is my hope that this decorated chest will guide the mason well, so his eyes might see through the darkness of our history.

26

PILGRIMS

It was towards the bottom of a field that lay beyond the last of the good grazing. Out there nothing could grow for it was swampy and waterlogged much of the year. It was out of shouting distance from the last workers in the strips. In places the yellowy grass was bald for many had trod this way, carving out a footpath that only the space of years would grow over.

Towards this a man walked purposefully. The sun was rising but he was oblivious to its beauty as he kept his head down. This was because upon his back he carried a great weight, a heavy stone jar in a wicker basket which was strapped to his shoulders. And this was not his only burden. Fastened to his belt were various purses which clinked as he walked, but his hands were free and now and again he stopped to speak to a woman who followed behind, alike weighed down, with two heavy baskets on either arm, covered in white cloths.

They tramped away from the village early, with the first loaves and the little flat cakes which were so popular. The cinder track stopped and they stepped up onto the wooden duckboard which lay over the marshy part of the way.

This was a well defined path. The route had been made easy. Here and there some symbol or sign pointed out the direction. At the last turning was a stone crucifix where the faithful once prayed thinking on Christ's Gethsemane, his death for their redemption. The man and woman passed it without a bow. The man, for all his free hands, did not bless himself.

273

As they entered the field the woman looked around. The way to the shrine was unobstructed. She glanced at the man and set her baskets down then continued towards the ruin, where she knelt. The man unburdened himself of his container and rubbed his shoulders where the straps had bitten. He stretched and straightened up, feeling suddenly light, but the relief which surged into him did not last. He ached, so he squatted with his back propped against the jar, waiting until the woman was ready to rejoin him.

To one side of the low open field stood a sort of barn; a roughly made shed, it would not do for animals in winter, or even in heavy rain, but here the pilgrims slept.

They were an unruly, shambling brood – more like vagrants than holy men; beggars all and drunkards. Their women sounded like fishwives and carried on as whores. Common harlots, the last genuine palmer told the man. But there were no more real pilgrims making their way to the shrine these days. He made do with what custom there was.

Those women infuriated him with their white faces, dredged in flour that made them look more like cadavers than anything a spark of passion might inflame. They reddened their mouths with berry stains to open their lips over black teeth and wiggle their tongues at him, making jokes about his manhood. Shameless creatures, they pulled down their bodices at the front and wore them low upon their hips, swaggering between the men who milled around. Like clucking hens they went among whatever party gathered, calling and beckoning. And he could not get them off the field. They stayed long after the last groups had departed, setting fires and screeching. They terrified him. He dreaded their mocking glances, detested their pointed words.

Once this had been a place of proper prayer, although he scarce remembered it as such. But it used to be the best loved of the local shrines, keeping a steady number of visitors throughout the year, and busy on the feast day.

It was his father who taught him the trade of striking pilgrim badges. His father was an artisan. A proud man who told his son they could do better than simple cockle shells which were brought in from the shore, cleaned up and sold for a token. On account of his skill they would have proper lead badges as at all the famous shrines.

The man untied a string about his belt and released the larger of the purses. Inside it he kept the assortment he sold. Not that any of this gaggle would bother. They were intent upon their pleasure. However it was worth a try; some might still buy them to carry home and show suspicious wives and neighbours as evidence of a clear heart.

His wife, her prayers said, came towards him and lifted both her baskets. She moved towards the half open door of the shed, where she hesitated. They both knew better than to go inside. Who knew what villainy lurked; thieves and murderers who could cut a man's throat for something once said in anger.

The man joined her and shouted to announce his presence. In answer the door was kicked wide from within.

Inside, bodies lay on top of each other. The stench of sweat and sour air was overpowering. He stood in front of his wife so that she would not see their disgusting nakedness, but a half-clad man raced towards them then suddenly lurched and vomited, splattering them with the gorgings of his belly which steamed in the early morning quiet. Birds settled upon the pile and picked at it.

The man and woman, who some might take for trades people, crossed towards the shrine now that their presence had been noted. The man unplugged the stopper from the heavy jar and his wife took the cover off one of her baskets, showing warm loaves and the crisp baked tops of cakes.

The man was sickened. His father, and his father before him had cared for the shrine, and before that it had been in his family. He knew nothing else. He imagined it would be different if it were a popular place along a well travelled itinerary. Then there might be many people coming from different parts, always ready to speak of what they had seen and describe the places they came from, which were beyond the edge of his world. But that had all gone, not even the diseased came to touch their tired sores against the amulet. He had that in his keeping.

In his grandfather's time there were riots, pushing and shoving to get close as it was held aloft. Women past their time begged to be allowed to hold it to their bellies. Everyone wanted to touch the smooth black stone which warmed against the skin and seemed to glow. But lately it behaved as if it had been stripped of its properties for it would not effect any cures. It had never helped his wife. It used to have its own box, but now he carried it around in his belt. Even a cutpurse would not bother with it.

And while every day he watched the shrine, kept it clean and so served the holy woman's resting place, he felt it mocked him. Each day his wife knelt at it before those snoring in ale were awake and arguing. He told himself that at least one true prayer still rose in this place, from one good woman like sweet balm among all the human wreckage, a bright jewel among the worthless souls. But these honest supplications fell upon the stones, deaf and unyielding in a ruined tower which the harlots desecrated.

A sad shrine, so old its story was lost in the telling. Some called the early martyr Scolastii, in other parts she was known as Clothilde. A nun in orders, and her power was such that a childless woman gaining an audience with her would return the next year to give thanks with a full womb or a babe upon her knee.

Although the habit was dying out, there were still some couples who came from the village to pray at the ruin. But it was more as an old custom that they had forgotten the meaning of. Many did not need it, their bellies already showed good sign of increase as they stood nervous as brides, their union fruitful by so early an intent. And his good wife, barren these last five years. The man wept at times when he thought of the years ahead. What would become of the place when they were gone, with no sons to take it over? And worse, what might happen to her if he were to die? She was too old to be taken as a wife a second time.

The whores had names for him. They laughed, called him Pinchstick and Little Flat Bladder, and claimed to cure him for a price. He was terrified of their eyes, and those awful tongues. To be the object of such women's pity was cruelty beyond measure.

But this day he was weary. Heavy in his heart, he watched his wife. He had maintained the shrine for no purpose, no miracles or cures were ever known to him. Now plans were afoot to discredit the name of Scolastii, and Clothilde, to prove that the woman did not live, or if she did she was not the same Clothilde who was a healer. Nowhere was there a record of the martyrdom. Now it was all so difficult. Once a saint was made by popular demand, and by the bishop, if he could be persuaded that it would benefit the clergy. But not any more. Now such matters were decided in Rome by distant figures who knew nothing of their lives here. Their local saint was insignificant to these men. But did anyone care? Only he, and he freely admitted to himself that he cared because it was his livelihood.

And, true to form, the stories and the miracles had dried up. In his father's time, women had walked for days to kneel and beg to be rid of the flux. He heard tell of women spared the madness after birth and of others whose travail was made easy by the good woman who had the cure for milk-fever and red-rash. There were stories of endless bleeding which stopped after years, and of wasting and paleness all discharged.

He still made badges. He cast them in wax first, as he had learnt, for it was his trade. But he made them crudely, lacking the skill of his father. In his day good women wore them around their necks throughout their waiting and clutched them tightly to their bellies as the first pangs took them. But the bigger sites called them now, and this place was left to the harlots who drew their custom from the sad and desperate men who travelled from the south; the poor who could make it to no other place.

He would only give to those who could pay, and he despised them. No one in the village would give hospitality to the types who settled upon the fields and stones to while away their afternoons.

When he was still a boy, the last great miracle had been denounced as a fraud. A blind man ran down to the church screaming he could see. But the priest recognised the man from another pilgrimage where he had taken the waters and been miraculously cured there too. He was denounced as a false pilgrim and his father was tried for bribing the man to act. But they could not prove this, for whatever the blind man said, he was already known to be a liar so no charges were ever made. But his father suffered.

Once the man had been quick to see to all the jobs, but he was tired. Now moss grew on the tower. He kept it neat in the past; he would scrape the stones clean. But it was a thankless task. It did not feel like a real shrine. Drunken men desecrated the walls with their hot, yellow piss and performed all manner of gross acts under cover of night. But their souls were as naked to God as in the keenest day.

He was watched. On Wednesday last the clerk rode out to write inside his ledger the sum of rent the man paid each season to the church. His family had long established rights to the place, even before the shrine, when all the land was bare. In those times his people had cultivated the area. One of his forefathers had a receipt, which he passed down, for shifting the stone needed in building the tower before the time of darkness. Great monasteries once dominated the land. Now it was an empty, wind-blown place. It offered no shelter, although the revellers did not mind. The seclusion aided their evil purposes.

He had watched the clerk enter in his book the meaningless lines which meant that he had paid and was discharged his debt for the time.

'This day of the Lord, the fourth of April, being the month of *hoeing, in the year twelve hundred and ninety-one, anno Domini, received as tithes for ancient rites upon the land, commonly known as Jynette's Field, wherein is the disputed shrine of one such holy nun, the sum of fifteen silver denier.'*

In dark soil the pale shape was moulded, its flush, smooth surface polished by each grain of sand escaping from mountainous stone. Earth thought to preserve the skull and ribs, sealing in their memory with its damp embrace, a careful lover, taking time. Inside the clear head moss took root, sprouting from the blind sockets that once witnessed a long dead world passing before them.

He watched as the clerk filled in the amount in black upright lines. Then he called his wife and she came forward to put a cross where he pointed on the page.

This morning he could not explain his heavy-heartedness. But he felt that they should move on. For the following period they were both too busy to think as the travellers came to buy, and the hands were quick in the baskets pulling at things and pouring drink down their throats.

Their speech and manners were foul. Many of this crowd seemed to know each other from previous visits, or from walking the roads. They were people who had been cast adrift, without home or welcome anywhere. He looked at the men's faces. They were coarse featured, scarred and pitted, with red veined noses and broken skin. They sweated and stank. But there was a similarity about them beyond appearance. They were a different tribe, more definite than the last, not solitary men but a band who recognised in each other a common identity. And he dreaded that he might become one of them.

For the first time he felt defeated, as if a battle somewhere had been lost. He no longer cared for the shrine. Let it be taken over then and used by those who would. His face was set and stern for the remainder of the day, and that evening his wife was not surprised when he said that he wanted her to journey to her family.

'I will join you after I have made sound our debts.'

'But what about your rights to the land?' she warned, for his feeling was always strong. But he shook his head slowly.

'There's no grazing in it, and you know I'm not a farmer. I don't care to lease it any more. Let the church have it,' and he laughed for the first time in a long while when he thought the church could sort the pilgrims out. Already it was peopled with its own kind.

'We'll go to a more popular place, begin there. You'll see.'

But he knew how jealously these patches were kept. It was legend how his grandmother, a tall strong woman with a hand span as great as any man's, once fought off a baker who thought to sell loaves here.

His wife nodded obediently. If she had doubts she did not let him see them. She nodded while they faced destitution. He took this to mean her agreement.

27

REFLECTIONS

EVERYTHING WAS SILENT. THE nun crossed the courtyard where only the day before the shouts of pupils had filled her ears. She had survived another year into a dead and silent summer.

Now with school closed Cecile felt that she was not a part of anything. She had ceased to believe that she was part of life in the convent a few years ago after her nervous illness. They said that she was unaccustomed to being an invalid, that she reacted badly. A terrible patient they all said, who ran rings around Sister Anselm and refused to rest. But her eagerness to be rid of such ill health had been a mistake. While she forced her body to perform its usual movements, obstinately defying the illness, it must have worked its mischief on her any other way it could. Long after she was pronounced recovered, the malaise still lingered. It tainted everything she saw. It hung about her and poisoned the air. She awoke to a life that was empty while all around her were voices congratulating her on a speedy recovery.

She understood then how she must carry on. She still had a function, for while the school was open she was a teacher first and foremost. It was when they shut for holidays that she could not cope. For what was she then? Not a nun; an imposter in the order who was too old to change her life and so remained among them like a memory. She was left with the faintest impression of sand writing where she had once carved her belief in stone.

Her health generally was not good. She was old, but this year she had declined rapidly. Now she only gave tutorials to sixth form groups which followed a general course with Sister Joseph. At least she still had a role. Without it she would wash away as the last traces do when the tide pulls back, leaving nothing but a scum of foam, the spit of contempt for a wasted life.

She could not hope to teach a full timetable again. The steep flight of stairs in the main building alone would have defeated her, but she knew she lacked the stamina to face class after class. She worried that her dishonesty might show through, that she would blurt out what she knew, that there was nothing. She had offered her life to an ideal only to discover that it did not exist.

Nowadays the chaplain brought communion to her, the chapel steps were too much of an effort. She accepted the cold sacrament each week, a ritual without meaning, and throughout the day she would find herself absently reciting prayers. She performed the minimum rites to allow herself to merge into the convent and remain silent within her own secret world, which was not a world of disbelief, of healthy, rational argument, of disputes to be taken up and discussed, but a world that had lost something. A world whose centre had been removed. Cecile faced belief's absence. And it was horrifying.

On reaching the other side of the courtyard she drew up a massive bunch of keys which hung around her waist. She rummaged through them. She could not remember what half of them were for. Selecting a long key, she fitted it into the lock and struggled with the main school door.

Within a week the builders would move in and gut the lower floor to make the small music rooms into a laboratory. How many laboratories did they need? She had never studied science. It wasn't considered proper for a girl. Here were great unexplained mysteries, science said, and here were the tools to explain them. And would everything be solved? One day, would it all be laid out in a text book – life, death? It frightened her because she was at the end of life, peering at the emptiness which lay beyond. But wasn't that what she wanted? To stop. A complete end. Still she was not prepared for it. Who was, after a life-time? Wasn't that what made them crawl snivelling to priests?

She couldn't. She had been deserted. Just when she needed it most her faith sloped off and left her to whistle after it.

Inside the corridor she waited for a moment, breathing lavender wax and chalk. She remembered how she had once been, rushing from class to class with a full teaching load and not enough hours in the day. She had so wanted to produce something that would make her mark as a historian, not merely a teacher. She had at last been able to submit her paper on monasticism two years ago. It was well received. A seminal work they called it, but she knew it could promise nothing more from her. She had no time left to develop the ideas in it. Someone else would do that, there would be no further essays from her pen. She had spent her life disciplined, devoted to God and the service of others. That one paper had become her life's work and her peak. She would not repeat it.

Oh, yes, and she must not forget the tablecloth. All in the service of others. The border painstakingly stitched. And of course there were all the girls who passed under her watchful eye as pupils. All in a life's work. She thought it was a sad tribute to her lost years of research.

She pulled herself up the first flight of stairs, and on the first landing sat on the top step to recover her strength. She could see down the stairwell. Some of the classrooms had doors open. Inside, the rows of desks stared insolently back, a silent ink-stained regiment with their battle scars, initials gouged in their sides.

It might take her a long time to get to chapel, but she was determined to go there. She wanted to see the marvellous painting one more time. It was beautiful, the treasure of the order. All sorts of people came out to see it. Experts, lecturers, they had even made a series about early painting and asked for permission to come and film it. Now there were postcards in art shops and in museums which bore on the back the phrase 'In a private collection. Saint Polycarp and an unknown family group, c.1350–1360'.

Their financial worries had not been eased by the panel's authenticity, although now they received revenue from postcards, from rights to photograph the panel, and from educational works; they also remained on good terms with the museum and had loaned the work for an exhibition last year.

No one understood what it meant to her. That something endured undetected, surviving until it was ready to be seen. Their care of the painting was at last justified, for it had been dear to the convent, and now it was an accolade that they should have preserved it so carefully. It was due to the care of generations of sisters that it survived, and the order could feel rightfully proud.

She had been privileged to see it unfold, become as new and offer its secrets. But they could make little of them. That was what excited Cecile, the potential for so much; it held a key to the past. She wondered if anyone would give a convincing explanation of the three figures? For generations it would be a puzzle picture, but she did not doubt that someone yet to be born would one day solve it.

What was that man's name? He had tried so hard ... Wainsmouth, was it? And the big Catholic man – jolly fellow – who was he? That was the year she had been ill. The painting was waiting on her recovery with such light and hope. They had brought it in to her. The small man carried it like a bridegroom across the threshold. But she had not reacted as she ought. Something terrified her; the illness still clawing at her nerves must have made her sensitive. She dreaded seeing the saint's face. She began to shake. They were disappointed. She could not explain, but she felt that there was something dangerous in the painting. She tried to smile, but they saw her frown. It was the virus, clinging to her, making her skeletal and light-headed. The tower disturbed her. She felt trapped, imprisoned by ignorance and there was no way of knowing.

That year her best student had changed direction, late on in the year. She had come to her sheepishly to say that she doubted her religious fervency and Cecile was scared by her own reaction, one of delight. She felt the prison crumble, as if something inside her had gone. Siobhan could soar at last without constraint, like the dove in the painting. A young woman now, leading her own life.

When last she heard, Siobhan was off to America. Before that, Cecile had only seen her once when she was still at university in the Midlands. She remembered that her dark hair had been cut very short, and that she seemed subdued. Cecile urged her to take whatever opportunities came up. She hoped that she had.

She pulled herself up and walked up the next flight, wishing that she had never sat down. To stop always made it hard to resume. Restarting was the most difficult part. Next time if she had to rest she would simply lean on the banister, she would not attempt to lower herself. The muscles in her legs ached. She knew that she would never set foot inside her stock room again, unless she requested they carry her, an odd request from a doting old woman, but she would never do that. It wasn't her room anyway, never had been really. Now it housed all manner of junk she heard tell, apparently it had found use as a lost property office. The receptacle for all the lone socks and plimsolls in the world. Lost property; she thought of her great finds, that's all they were really. The amulet was one of these magical stones they were so fond of in the Middle Ages, they handed them out like prescriptions. The little pilgrim's badge must have belonged to someone who had been away, but they could not identify the shrine. Not from the Holy Land, no palm; they could not place it. But these items were not rare and it took its place among a collection held at the county museum. The wooden container, which was a mould for a reliquary to be beaten against, was also on display at the same museum. All they retained, apart from the stone, was the piece of parchment, a curiosity on account of its age. They had it framed and now it hung in a dark corner of the school library where it was seldom noticed. But she was thankful for the chance she had had to be present as the painting slowly became whole again. To have lived through such excitement. Both the restorers said there would not be another one like it in their lifetimes. It was rare to have such an opportunity in an entire career.

It had been a strange year, a disturbing time. But it was an undercurrent rather than a great gale. It softly blew things away, leaving everything altered, and after it the panel stood refreshed. But she was irritated because it was a mystery still to be solved and she was at the end of her life. She would not see its resolution.

Fact became submerged after the passage of time. People moved away, changed, were lost, and their lives forgotten. She had already lost track of Siobhan; she was not even sure of the names of the two restorers any more. No wonder the painting would not yield its story.

There was not enough evidence to make any definite claims to the identities of the three figures who so mysteriously stood in the background now. After being hidden for so long, they remained furtive, but the theory of the monk, the nun and their child was the one they chose as the most likely explanation. Yet the tower stood over them like a question mark and Cecile knew it had not been solved.

On the second landing she stood still for a minute before crossing the passageway into the chapel. Inside it was cold and gloomy. She felt along the wall for the light switch and saw the dirty marks where countless fingers had pressed. The weak afternoon light was not made stronger with the electric on. Over on the altar a stalwart little red lamp burned inside a golden container. In the draught of the open door it flickered. Cecile shut the door quickly and for a moment the flame, fanned in a breeze, flared up, then it seemed to die quite suddenly. She looked for the matches which were always at hand to keep the lamp burning. Such a little flame to signify the presence of God. She struck a match, but stood by the altar uncertain of what to do. She let it burn down and blew it out just as it reached her fingers. While she was there, there was no need of a flame to remind her of God's presence. The light died and on the altar was God's absence.

If anyone disturbed her she would pretend she had not noticed.

'Oh, has the lamp gone out?' she would ask and offer the matches to them.

A shaft of sun made the stained glass colours appear on the opposite wall. If she passed her hand through the ray she broke it, her shadow wiped out all the brilliance which played in specks of light to camouflage the pale yellow paint. Such fragile impressions they were, to be destroyed by the movement of her hand, or the turn of her head. But there was six hundred years of permanence on the altar. That was what she wanted to see. She sat on a bench to view the panel. It was placed behind the altar at its centre. Originally it would have been only a side section in a much larger work. It was part of an altarpiece and probably not considered important when it was broken up, which could account for it surviving. They had suggested that the three figures were added later, maybe someone bought the fragment and commissioned a painter to include a local story, or the artist – who, they told her, had been trained in Italy – remembered a tale from his childhood and being far from home included it in his work.

Now that this panel was on its own she felt that the figures loomed out of all proportion. She tried to envisage the effect they might have had, tucked away and barely visible on an altarpiece teeming with saints and scenes from a life. Possibly they meant nothing to anyone except the artist who put them there; maybe a traveller, coming from the same part, stood in front of it and was put in mind of a tale he once heard in his childhood, distant and faint. Yet she was haunted by it. And that tower. Why was it there? If she closed her eyes she still saw its imprint in the sightless world behind her eyelids, like the outline of a window frame on a sunny day when she turned her face away.

That tower, like the dancing pieces of stained glass, burned upon her vision long after she ceased to look at it. In her dreams it had been silent, waiting, yet it showed her no door or window. There was no way she might enter its heart.

Lately her dreams were calmer. Today, confronting the painting, she understood that the tower's strength was its endurance. It existed, and that was its triumph, no matter that she could not understand. It would outlive her, outlive all of them, just as Saint Polycarp had. Despite his age they put him to death and so assured his legend. The saint lived on. But who could say who first accused him, or name the one who lit the fire to burn his mortal self?

Surely that was immortality, she thought. Death could be the quietest of sleeps, death without eternity would be peaceful. The promise of judgment and retribution was what disturbed her. But immortality need not be that frightening continuation of life, of sensibility, but something other. And she realised that her own history, because of memory, could not be Godless.

The painting glowed. Deep crimson and gold warmed the saint's flesh as he stood, forever stating his innocence. No heretic, no false prophet, he pointed to his chest where a pure heart beat.

The new wooden frame revealed the painting in its entirety. The old eighteenth-century frame had been re-gilded and stood emptily in a niche waiting for an image to fill it, like an empty mirror.

Cecile blessed herself out of habit. She would leave now. The child, the nun and the monk stood as a group, arranged that way by the artist. She wondered if they had ever been a group, or whether they were placed together out of aesthetic design only. The small tower was next to them. As she extinguished the light she glanced back. It had all but faded from view. The gloom covered its outlines and even when she squinted she could not make it out. She thought how the ability to hide could save a smaller animal's life when threatened by a larger. Its disappearance was a sign of its survival.

She blessed herself again automatically at the door. Her descent from chapel would be painful. She would not return. Some day the tower would reappear in a brighter light than she had been able to cast. One day its story might be discovered. But not yet.

The painting stared out at her retreating back; for now it would rest inviolate. And in a strange sense, the old nun felt relieved.

Under the weight of soil the skull cracked open like a half-egg. Earth filled the hollow that remained. The place where every dream and thought played out its existence, until soundless, sightless end put paid to further schemes.

Clay cradled it and, like a jealous mother, hugged close the naked memory of bones. These splintered to scatter as dun and yellow fragments, and so nourished the earth.

Bone does not count eternity grain by grain. It leaves no timer at the world's end, except sometimes a random fossil, a footprint of history. Bone disintegrates in a steady silence that is carried on the wind and settles imperceptibly as dust.

Penelope Fitzgerald

The Gate of Angels

Cambridge, 1912: rational young scientist Fred Fairly falls off his bike only to wake in bed and in love with a stranger – Brixton nurse and fellow casualty, Daisy, who takes up Fred's education, questions his questioning, and pinpoints finally quite what is the matter.

'Contains more wit, intelligence and feeling than many novels three times its length. If confirms Fitzgerald's place as one of the finest and most entertaining novelists writing in England today.'
Michael Ratcliffe, *Observer*

'This is an achievement – a metaphysical novel which is entertaining, brief, and a love story. The book's shortness and sparseness, combined with the complexity of its concerns, is a miracle of technique.'   Victoria Glendinning, *The Times*

'Penelope Fitzgerald writes books whose imaginative wholeness and whose sense of what language can suggest is magical. Whichever way you twist the lens of this kaleidoscopic book, you see fresh things freshly.'   Candia McWilliam, *Standard*

flamingo

Sara Suleri

Meatless Days

'This is virtuoso self-expression. It marks a daunting literary debut.'
Clive Fisher, *Financial Times*

'A *tour de force* of memory and interpretation . . . What makes *Meatless Days* such an astonishing book is its corrosive effect on partitions of all kinds – between body and history, politics and poetry, language and experience, the East and the West. Suleri seems to find nourishment in the most indigestible truths. Beware her prose at its most luscious: cunningly – appetizingly – enfolded in a mango leaf, a mouthful of stones awaits.'
Village Voice

'An extraordinary first book. The reader retains a sensation of infinite sadness at losses so irreplaceable that life seems bleached of possibilities. As an evocation of family love, with all its sharpness, pain and need, *Meatless Days* is almost faultless.'
Caroline Moorehead, *New Statesman*

'A super-subtle book . . . Suleri writes with a surgical intellectual frankness, and combines a slightly distorted syntactical elegance with an unusual clarity of diction. Dislocation makes for a poetic precision which crisps the reader into paying absolute attention.'
Candia McWilliam, *London Review of Books*

'Worthwhile reading? Very. It is unique.'
Rumer Godden, *Daily Telegraph*

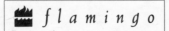 *flamingo*

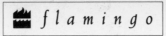 *flamingo*

Flamingo is a quality imprint publishing both fiction and non-fiction. Below are some recent titles.

Fiction
☐ The Things They Carried *Tim O'Brien* £4.99
☐ Matilda's Mistake *Anne Oakley* £4.99
☐ Acts of Worship *Yukio Mishima* £4.99
☐ My Cousin, My Gastroenterologist *Mark Leyner* £4.99
☐ Escapes *Joy Williams* £4.99
☐ The Dust Roads of Monferrato *Rosetta Loy* £4.99
☐ The Last Trump of Avram Blok *Simon Louvish* £4.99
☐ Captain Vinegar's Commission *Philip Glazebrook* £4.99
☐ Gate at the End of the World *Philip Glazebrook* £4.99
☐ Ordinary Love *Jane Smiley* £4.99

Non-fiction
☐ A Stranger in Tibet *Scott Berry* £4.99
☐ The Quantum Self *Danah Zohar* £4.99
☐ Ford Madox Ford *Alan Judd* £6.99
☐ C. S. Lewis *A. N. Wilson* £5.99
☐ Meatless Days *Sara Suleri* £4.99
☐ Finding Connections *P. J. Kavanagh* £4.99
☐ Shadows Round the Moon *Roy Heath* £4.99
☐ Sweet Summer *Bebe Moore Campbell* £4.99

You can buy Flamingo paperbacks at your local bookshop or newsagent. Or you can order them from Fontana Paperbacks, Cash Sales Department, Box 29, Douglas, Isle of Man. Please send a cheque, postal or money order (not currency) worth the purchase price plus 22p per book (or plus 22p per book if outside the UK).

NAME (Block letters)_____

ADDRESS_____

_____

_____